A Guide to
Common Reef Fishes
of the Western Indian Ocean

K. R. Bock

photographs by J. Mackinnon
and Ian Took

MACMILLAN
PUBLISHERS

First published 1978
Reprinted 1985

Published by *Macmillan Publishers Ltd*
London and Basingstoke
*Associated companies and representatives Accra,
Auckland, Delhi, Dublin, Gaborone, Hamburg, Harare,
Hong Kong, Kuala Lumpur, Lagos, Manzini, Melbourne,
Mexico City, Nairobi, New York, Singapore, Tokyo*

ISBN 0 333 23977 6

Printed in Hong Kong

Contents

Acknowledgements

In the descriptions of the fishes, I have drawn deeply from the published work of the late Professor J.L.B. Smith and Margaret M. Smith; from their two invaluable books (*Sea Fishes of Southern Africa* and *The Fishes of Seychelles*) and also from Professor Smith's many Icthyological Bulletins. This book could not have been written without constant reference to these sources: they will remain an outstanding contribution to the natural history of Western Indian Ocean waters. Margaret Smith herself has been patient and understanding in dealing with my many, often naive, queries. I am very much in her debt.

I have also drawn on several other scientific papers and books, a list of the more significant of which is included in the references given at the end of the book. I make no apologies for having contributed little of value myself; the urgent need for a simple specific guide to the common fishes of our reefs will, I hope, be sufficient justification for my temerity, as a non-specialist, in preparing this work.

The excellent photographs were taken by my colleagues Jeannie Mackinnon and Ian Took. I am deeply indebted to them for their major contribution.

My very special thanks go to my family, both for their company and assistance in gathering data and material, and for their patience while the manuscript was written.

Mr Solomon Gichuhi typed the manuscript and Dr John Guthrie criticised it: I am most grateful to them both. Dr H.E. Belcher kindly checked Chapter Seven for me.

Preface

The incentive to devote much of my spare time to preparing this introduction to the common reef fishes of the Western Indian Ocean was prompted, in part at least, by memories of my own frustrations when first trying to identify them. For many of us, the thrill and enchantment of the underwater world gives way, sooner or later, to a desire to put a name to whatever we are looking at.

The obvious course of action is to purchase a good illustrated book on tropical fish, but I found that this tended initially to add to, rather than detract from, frustration: there was, apparently, no easy way of becoming acquainted with the names of a bewildering number of species. Whenever opportunity offered itself, I studied those two excellent reference books, J.L.B. Smith's *The Sea Fishes of Southern Africa,* and Smith and Smith's *The Fishes of Seychelles.* This is all very well for an addict; the majority of people have neither the inclination nor the time to spend hours tracking through a reference book, however good it is, in the hope of spotting one particular species out of hundreds of illustrations.

Other books on tropical reef fish (there are several good ones) have different limitations. They cover tropical fishes in general, and, inevitably, only a small proportion of the illustrations are of species which occur locally: they often make no attempt to inform the reader whether the species described or illustrated are common and widespread, or rare.

I have tried to overcome some of these problems by describing and illustrating about one hundred and twenty species that the average observer is likely to encounter in two hours quiet goggling at low tide. I have also written brief descriptive notes of a further fifty allied species. All of these occur throughout the Western Indian Ocean, although their presence and relative abundance in any one place is quite naturally dependent upon the overall characteristics of the local habitat. These considerations are dealt with in detail in Chapter Three.

All the fishes described occur in shallow water, from the shore line to about five metres depth. Mask and snorkel with flippers or tennis shoes are the only equipment necessary to enjoy fully the tropical reefs.

I have included three chapters on the environment which, I hope, will add to the interest of fish watching. There is a brief description of the waters of the Indian Ocean, because a knowledge of the characteristics of the sea that washes our reefs is fundamental to an understanding of the growth and development of corals. The coral reef is the particular and special environment of the fishes described, and for this reason I have added two chapters on corals and coral reefs.

There are two chapters on fishes. The first is an introduction to their external form and to certain terms used to describe a fish. This is necessary to appreciate fully the adaptation of many species to their various highly specialised ways of life. I have followed this with a generalised account of a few of the more outstanding attributes of coral fish, such as their brilliant or remarkably cryptic coloration.

Another reason for this book is the obvious and very urgent need for the conservation and preservation of the reefs of the Western Indian Ocean. Much is being done to ensure their survival with the establishment of systems of Marine National Parks and Reserves. Kenya and the Seychelles are foremost in this endeavour and are happy and outstanding examples of accepting responsibility to safeguard a natural resource of international significance and interest. But in order to ensure a wider appreciation of the wonders of the reef, it is necessary to inform people. This small publication will, I hope, stimulate first an interest, then an awareness, and finally a clear perception that reefs are indeed a priceless national heritage.

In a world hastening to its own suicidal doom with overcrowding and with noisesome technology, coral reefs are tranquil, wild places where man can restore at least some part of his battered soul.

1 Waters of the Western Indian Ocean

The sea fishes of the Western Indian Ocean are generally described as Indo-Pacific. The Indo-Pacific region stretches eastwards from the African coast, to include the South-East Asian Islands and archipelagos, the Northern and Great Barrier Reef areas of Australia, and the Central and Southern Pacific Ocean, as far east as the Hawaiian Islands.

While the distribution of strong ocean-going swimmers such as marlin, sailfish or tunny affords no great problems, there are many species of fish which are weak, feeble swimmers and yet they are common to reefs of both the Pacific Islands and the African coast. A study of the principal currents of the Indian Ocean in relation to those of the Pacific affords an immediate answer to the distribution of fishes over this enormously wide area.

The key is the South Equatorial Current, which flows continuously from east to west throughout the year, drawing water from the Pacific Ocean, as shown in Maps 1 and 2 (inside front and back covers), from about April to October, and from the Indonesian region from November to March. This current impinges on the African coast at about 10°S latitude, at Cape Delgado in Mozambique. Here it diverges into the southward flowing Mozambique Current and the northward flowing East African Coastal Current. The origins of these two important coastal currents help explain why a Kenyan or Somali skindiver off the southern Mozambique, Seychellois or Mauritian reefs finds himself among a remarkably familiar fish fauna. It also explains why J. B. Smith's book *The Sea Fishes of Southern Africa* is invaluable in the identification of a great number of fishes of Eastern Africa and the islands of the Western Indian Ocean.

One does not need a strong imagination to visualise tiny fish larvae, or small fishes themselves, being moved by local tidal currents into the main flow of water from the Pacific, through the Torres Straits north of Australia. Possibly afforded some protection by a mass of floating weed or flotsam, and given a very great amount of luck indeed, the survivors will ultimately arrive in shallower waters off the eastern coast of Africa.

Here they may find a habitat suited to their needs. And then, from coral to coral, or patch of weed to patch of weed, over a vast span of time, their descendants will slowly move northwards or southwards, exploiting a familiar reef environment as they go. They have done more than this; by the processes of natural selection new species have arisen which are related to, but different from, species occurring in the extremities of the eastern Pacific. I have no idea at what rate successful transits are made from the Australian or Indonesian regions to the African coast, but I imagine they are not at all frequent. I also suspect some families are hardier (or luckier) than others; Blennies, for example, are great travellers but they could hardly be called swimmers. Yet some of the most widely distributed of all species are found among them.

The East African Coastal Current (EACC) flows northwards from Cape Delgado, along the Tanzania and Kenya coasts, the ultimate extent of its northernmost limit being dependent on the Monsoon or trade winds.

From April to October the south-east monsoon blows and, under its direction, the EACC continues its northerly flow at about four knots past the Kenya and Somali coasts. The south-east monsoon is a strong trade wind, blowing steadily at well over ten knots. In November, its season spent, it gives way to the north-east monsoon, which blows from November to March. Although a less forceful wind, it assists in generating the Somali Current, which flows southwards, to meet the EACC, now flowing at under one knot, off the north Kenya coast. These two currents deflect each other eastwards and join to form the Equatorial Counter Current.

The average monthly temperatures of the surface waters of the EACC vary from 29°C in March to 25°C in September; they are of high salinity and are oxygen saturated. If, during the south-east monsoon, a weighted line is lowered into the sea some distance off shore, it will tend to drift northwards, being pulled in that direction by the EACC. At about 120 metres depth the line will suddenly drift southwards, indicating that the weighted end has reached a strong southward flowing current or layer at that depth. This layering of the sea is known as stratification, and there are four major currents flowing at varying depths and in opposite directions in the Western Indian Ocean. These layers beneath the EACC need not concern us further, although they would certainly do so if this book were concerned with ocean-going, deeper-swimming fish.

During the south-east monsoon the depth of the EACC is greatest, being 110-120 metres, and its temperature falls only a fraction of a degree between the surface (27.3°C) and 100 metres (27.1°C). Beyond this depth there is a rapid fall in temperature with a small decrease in depth: from 27°C to 19°C in 22 metres. (Such rapid falls in temperature with small decreases in depth are known as thermoclines). In the north-east monsoon, the EACC is less deep, averaging about 85 metres and its temperature at this depth is 19°C, with a typical thermocline apparent over the last 11 metres.

The depth of the EACC must now be examined in relation to that of the continental shelf. The continental shelf is a continuation of the continent beneath the sea, and is usually taken to extend to the 180 metre contour. Beyond this point, the land mass generally falls off rapidly (the continental slope) to the depths of the ocean floor. The continental shelf off the coast of Eastern Africa is decidedly narrow, extending on average not more than 3 to 8 kilometres off shore. Within this distance, the 45 metre contour is highly significant as this is the maximum depth at which reef-building corals will thrive. The water moving over the reef is therefore always warm tropical water, and the colder, deeper, stratified layers never reach the reefs. As will be seen in the next chapter, this allows for the development of fringing coral reefs along most of the Eastern African coast and around the granitic and volcanic islands of the Indian Ocean.

2 The Reef-building Corals

Corals are fairly choosy animals. They require, for optimum growth, light, high temperatures, and sea water of high oxygen content, which must also be reasonably clear of fine sediments. In other words, they thrive only in warm, clear, shallow seas. These general remarks pertain to the reef-building corals in particular. There are corals which grow in the cold waters of northern seas, and others which eke out an existence in comparatively deep cool water, but they are mostly solitary creatures. We are concerned here with those corals which are perhaps the most spectacular architects of the animal world (man not excepted). They have the capacity to build vast structures, sometimes more than a thousand miles long, of great beauty and of varying form and design.

Reef-building species of coral do not thrive much below fifty-five metres. This is an effect of light, and not one of temperature: the East African Coastal Current, for example, is extremely warm (27.1°C) at ninety metres, much deeper than the limits of coral growth. The reason for this limit remains an area of dissension among experts, although it seems that there is an acceptable hypothesis. Corals are hosts to a primitive unicellular protozoan, which is classified somewhere in that rather hazy, ill-defined border area between the animals and the plants. These small organisms, called *Zooxanthellae,* live and metabolise within the tissues of the coral. They possess chlorophyll, and thus bring to their association with corals the attribute of photosynthesis. It seems that corals and their *Zooxanthellae* live in a happy state of mutual benefit or symbiosis, the one being dependent on the other for normal vigorous growth. As the *Zooxanthellae* are chlorophyll-containing animals, they, like all green plants, require light to function properly. Somewhere around forty-five metres the light is presumably too diffuse and weak for the *Zooxanthellae,* the corals are deprived of their symbiotic assistance, and in turn find life too difficult and precarious to manage. The exact nature of this extraordinary symbiotic relationship is not known, but in addition to other effects, corals deprived of their *Zooxanthellae* are unable to deposit calcium, an element vital to the formation of their protective structures.

4

High water temperatures are essential for the growth of coral reefs. This may be verified crudely by observing that reefs are more or less restricted to tropical seas, and are virtually confined to regions between the tropics of Cancer and Capricorn. They occur only on the eastern shores of the continents (East Africa, north-eastern Australia, The Caribbean); cold currents originating in Antarctica and the Arctic wash the western shores. Corals do not grow where temperatures are below 18°C. Growth is more vigorous as the temperature increases and reaches an optimum at about 30°C; at not many degrees higher than this, they are killed. The temperature of tropical surface water in the Western Indian Ocean varies from 25-28°C, and thus approaches the optimum for corals.

That corals require clear, saline water may also be subjected to crude observational verification. There is always a break in the reef at the mouth of rivers, such as exists opposite the Tana river delta in Kenya or the Rufiji river delta in Tanzania. Rivers disgorge fresh water, which also carries loads of fine silt or mud. This combination of both fresh water and sediment effectively precludes coral growth, but in fact the presence of either creates adverse conditions. Relatively short immersion in fresh water will kill corals; this is simply an effect of osmosis.

Corals are static, sedentary beasts, and deposition of sediment on them presents the serious problem of suffocation. When we come to a description of the coral animals themselves, it will be seen that some species are able to cope with light layers of sediment rather better than others. They have a reasonably efficient mechanism for removing sediment, but their capabilities in this direction are distinctly limited.

Other conditions being favourable, corals thrive best when they are bathed continuously in oxygen-rich water, a factor which also assures a continual replenishment of their food supply. For all these reasons, the most luxuriant coral growths occur on the seaward side of the reef. While profuse growth does occur on the leeward side of reefs, it only does so where the water is sufficiently deep to permit continuous total immersion, including the periods of low spring tides.

The coral animal

Corals belong to the fairly large group of marine animals known as the **Coelenterates,** derived from the Greek *koilos,* hollow, and *enteron,* bowel or gut. They are also called the Cnidaria (*knide,* nettle), and both terms describe outstanding characteristics of the group. Included in the Coelenterates are the closely related sea anemones, and the more distantly related jelly-fish and Portuguese Man-o'-War.

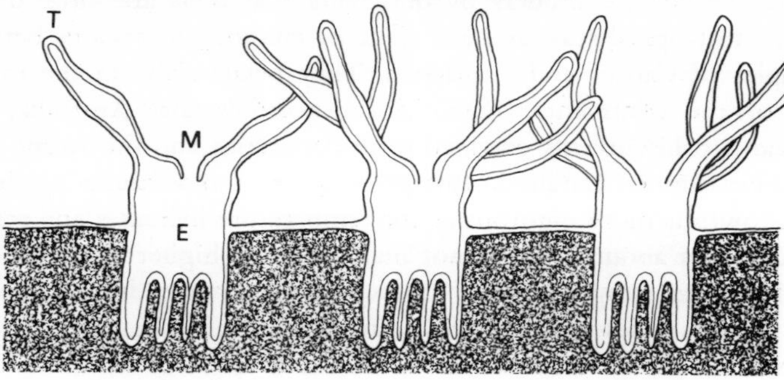

Cross-section of three adjacent coral polyps
T = tentacle   M = mouth   E = gut or enteron

T

M

E

Fig 1   *The builders of the reef*

The body consists of no more than an open or hollow sac, with the mouth as the single opening at one end. Coelenterates also bear stinging cells or **nematocysts**. These are specialised cells, usually arranged in batteries, and have coiled within them a barbed thread, itself often containing a neurotoxic type poison. When triggered, the lid of the cell opens and the thread is violently ejected as a tiny harpoon. Other cells contain sticky threads which assist in trapping the prey.

Fig. 1 illustrates three adjacent coral animals or **polyps** in a coral colony. The polyp is contained in a cup or theca of lime which it forms about itself by secretion. The coral polyps of a colony are joined to each other by a thin layer of living tissue.

They increase by a simple process of budding and thus their colonies grow in size, either radially in the rounded forms, or linearly in the branching tree-like and lobed or plate-like forms.

The mouth of the polyp is usually surrounded by numbers of nematocyst-bearing tentacles whose function is to trap and immobilise the prey by the nematocyst poison and then convey it by bending and contortion into the mouth. In the true or stony corals the tentacles are in sixes, or multiples of six. Around the mouth area or pharynx there are lines of hairs which, by beating in unison, are able to generate weak but effective currents: it is these which remove light sediments from the surface of the polyps.

While the increase in size of a coral colony is brought about by budding, at times male and female elements develop in the body tissues of the polyps. Eggs and sperm are released into the water, and the fertilized egg develops into a tiny larva, called the **planula,** which is motile. The larvae are part of the plankton for a time: they are dispersed passively by currents and, sooner or later, may be deposited on a surface which is

6

suitable for colonisation, such as firm rock. The planula grows into a polyp and begins to secrete calcium to form its protective cup, and initiates the process of budding. Thus are new favourable areas constantly exploited by the corals, and, potentially, are new reefs born.

Generally, the new coral colony will resemble closely the form of its progenitor, that is, plate-like forms will give rise to plate-like forms, and so on. This is not always so, however, as form is, with several species, a function of degree of turbulence of the water. For example, forms in calm, sheltered or in deeper water will differ from forms of the same species growing in strong flowing currents or tidal surges. The latter will tend to assume a shape giving least resistance to flow. This often adds to the great difficulties of species identification, coral species being among the most difficult of all animal groups.

Corals are rather slow-growing. Rounded species with massive forms grow some 10 millimetres a year; species with branching forms achieve 25 millimetres a year under optimal conditions. It can be estimated that the building of a reef represents a minimum of 7,000 to 10,000 years of ceaseless coral endeavour.

Although the reef foundation is an extremely solid structure, the growing periphery is an extremely brittle one, easily liable to damage which takes a very long time to mend. As such, both unintentional damage and breakages due to clumsy fishermen, gogglers or divers, and intentional damage by blasting the reef with explosives or by collecting corals for sale, are all most reprehensible.

The reef is subject to a great many natural forces of erosion and destruction: it has been said correctly that any reef represents the balance between forces of construction (the corals themselves, and other cementing agencies such as lime-secreting encrusting algae) and forces of destruction. It is continuously subjected to the battering of the waves of the sea, to tidal surges, and to storms. Many animals bore into the reef, thus weakening its structure. Coral polyps themselves form an important or exclusive article of diet of several families of reef fish, notably Parrot fish. That notorious predator of corals, the Crown-of-Thorns starfish *Acanthaster planci,* has destroyed areas of reef in the Pacific and off Queensland.

Much has been said about the recent population explosion of the Crown-of-Thorns starfish. This attractive species is present in the western Indian Ocean, mostly in low numbers, but in places there are dense local concentrations. There are two schools of thought concerning it: one maintains that as a result of man's activities, the balance has been tipped in favour of a massive increase in population. For example, the over-exploitation of natural enemies such as the Triton shell *Charonia tritonis,* off Queensland, which is a heavy predator of starfish, has resulted in a build-up of numbers. The other school maintains that we might be witnessing no more than a recurrent or cyclic increase in numbers, which probably occurs at infrequent intervals. This, it is argued, is in some way necessary for the genetic stability of the species as a whole. The answer may well lie somewhere between the two conflicting theories.

The Crown-of-Thorns starfish illustrates an interesting, though greatly puzzling, attitude of mankind. The depredation of corals by this echinoderm and the consequent destruction of relatively limited areas of the Australian and Pacific reefs has, for some curious reason, excited the interest of the public. Man, the arch destroyer, has wrought far greater and more massive destruction to reefs all over the world. Much of this destruction has taken place within the last twenty-five years or so, and proceeds today at an accelerating rate. Reefs are plundered for shells and corals; hectares of lagoons are reduced to grey lifeless rubble; entire ecosystems are polluted. Yet none of this destruction, which is on a very grand scale indeed, has attracted the attention of the public in the manner of that of the Crown-of-Thorns. It seems that the constant fouling of his own nest is a matter of complete indifference to mankind at large.

3 Reefs and Reef Habitats

Three types of reef are recognised: fringing reefs, barrier reefs and atolls. Fringing reefs are in continuity with a land or island mass; this does not preclude a fringing reef being separated from the shoreline by a lagoon. They are mostly in close proximity to the shore (up to one kilometre) and the lagoon is in general relatively shallow (up to ten metres). Barrier reefs, on the other hand, are separated from the shore by relatively deep water, and are several kilometres or more distant. While it may appear that this distinction is rather subjective, this is not so, although it is sometimes necessary to resort to geology to be certain.

Atolls present no difficulties: they are ring or horseshoe shaped island reefs, which enclose lagoons of often remarkably uniform depth.

Charles Darwin saw the three forms as an evolutionary sequence, barrier reefs arising from fringing reefs, and atolls from barrier reefs. He collected data on reefs during his voyage in the *Beagle* (1831-1836) and from his observations deduced his theory on their origins. It is a remarkable fact that his theories remain more or less intact and are still accepted nearly one hundred and fifty years after their conception.

In the case of oceanic islands, Darwin maintained that fringing reefs developed first. If the island subsided, the fringing reef continued to grow upward and outward, until it was separated from the now diminished island by comparatively deep water. At this point it was no longer a fringing reef, but had evolved into a barrier reef. Finally, if subsidence continued the island ultimately disappeared beneath the surface of the sea, leaving a circular coral reef, or atoll. Accumulation of sediments within these circular reefs resulted in lagoons of very uniform depth.

The American geologist Daly saw the origins of barrier reefs and atolls as a direct result of a fall in sea level. Daly based his glacial-control theory on the locking up of sea water during the ice ages, which resulted in a fall in the level of the seas. When the sea level was lower than it is today, many island and continental shore lines were eroded by wave action to form flat platforms. These proved ideal surfaces for coral reefs when the level rose once more with the melting of the great ice sheets.

Corals flourished with the general amelioration of climate and, keeping pace with the rising sea level, formed barrier reefs and atolls on the now submerged platforms. Results of deep drilling on atolls have indicated that both theories are acceptable. Both geological processes, therefore, have played their part in the origins of the reefs of today, and both Darwin's and Daly's theories account satisfactorily for all the essential features of reefs, including the massive vertical thickness of the coral structures.

The African reef system, which stretches from Mozambique in the south to the Red Sea in the north, a distance of some 8,000 kilometres, is of the fringing type and there are no classical barrier reefs as occur off north-eastern Australia. The Western Indian Ocean volcanic islands such as Mauritius and the unique granitic Seychelles also have fringing reefs, but there are also huge atolls, such as Aldabra and Cosmoledo, in the area.

We may take the East African fringing reef as being reasonably typical of the region. Two forms of fringing reef are apparent: those fringing the mainland and larger islands, which are separated from the shore by a lagoon, and the reefs fringing smaller islands, which grow on the sub-merged island slope itself.

In the latter instance, soft corals often dominate the upper zones of the fringe, being exposed or partially exposed at low spring tides. The remainder of the submerged slope is frequently covered in a profusion of coral species of luxuriant growth. Small islands of this nature are unfortunately not common, and are usually situated some distance off-shore: as such, they are not readily accessible and are only infrequently visited.

Mainland fringing reefs typically enclose a lagoon, the stretch of water contained between the reef and the shore. The lagoons of the Western Indian Ocean are very variable in width, from less than 100 to more than 800 metres. Although some lagoonal habitats are similar to those of the seaward reef slope and support a similar fauna, they are ecologically distinct. This is not a question of depth, but a simple difference between quiet, sheltered waters inside the main reef and the turbulent waters of the outer reef slope. Because this book is concerned mainly with fishes occurring in easily accessible shallow water, my descriptions are confined to the great variety of lagoonal and reef platform habitats which are, quite literally, at the visitor's feet.

Fig. 2 opposite, is a diagrammatic representation of a cross-section of a typical fringing reef, the three main features being the lagoon, sometimes described as the reef flat, the reef platform and the reef slope. The reef platform is a slightly elevated solid platform built of consolidated debris derived from the reef front.

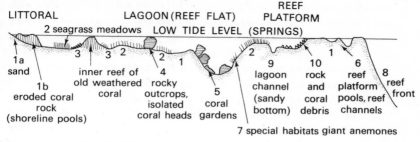

Vertical scale exaggerated. Occurrence and relative extent
of ecological zones vary considerably.

Fig. 2   *Diagrammatic cross section of a fringing reef*

The sea washes into or out of the lagoon along a system of channels
of varying width and depth, which cut through the reef. These drainage
channels are known locally in East Africa as *milango* (singular, *mlango*),
the Swahili for gateways. The deeper *milango* are areas of great interest,
sometimes supporting a profusion of coral growths, but should be
approached always with caution and respect as extremely strong currents
may be encountered in these areas.

Lagoonal habitats

In considering the lagoon transect shown in Fig. 2, it is perhaps unnecessary to mention that not all the habitats described necessarily occur
in any one locality, nor that the relative extent and sequence of each vary
greatly from place to place.

1) The substrate of the shoreline shallows may consist of sand, being an
extension of a gradually shelving sandy beach, or of a more or less flat
platform derived from an ancient eroded coral reef, containing tidal
pools. Neither habitat is subjected to violent wave action: the lagoon fills
quietly with the incoming tide, the main shock of the waves having been
broken and absorbed by the outer reef itself. Because of this, both habitats
are essentially sheltered ones.

a) Sandy shallows are not particularly rich in species, but they are far from
being barren. Frequently, especially on a rising tide, surprising concentrations of fish may be encountered. Species of Rays (Dasyatidae)
are often abundant; Pipefish (Syngnathidae), Sardine and Anchovies
(Clupeidae), Gerridae (especially *Gerres oyena*), sand-dwelling eels
(Myrichthidae), Lethrinidae (especially *Lethrinus harak*), and flatfish
(Soleidae) are found here, and also more generally about sandy areas
of the lagoon.

11

b) The shoreline tidal pools often sustain growth of seaweed and seagrass and afford ample cover and protection for many species. Together with the tidal pools of eroded ancient inner reefs and the reef platform, they constitute an important nursery area for young fish of many species. Perhaps the most typical residents of tidal pools are the Gobies, Blennies and Rockhoppers (Gobiidae, Blennidae and Salariidae), and there are areas where these interesting small fish positively dominate the inter-tidal scene. The very young of several species of Damselfish (Pomacentridae), Batfish (Platacidae) Grey Mullets (Mullidae) and even of Barracuda are found, often in great numbers. But the only common Butterfly fish juveniles regularly encountered are those of *Chaetodon lunula,* and more rarely, in the deeper pools, the young of Angelfish (Pomacentridae), particularly *Pomacanthops semicirculatus.*

2) Seagrass meadows often cover considerable areas of lagoons; the dark patches among the incredibly beautiful greens, blues and turquoise colours of the lagoon at low tides are stands of seagrass.

The dominant, most vigorous and most widespread species of seagrass is *Cymodocea* (Fig. 3), a flowering plant, and not a seaweed. Seagrass is also something of a misnomer, as *Cymodocea* and similar plants are more closely related to the freshwater pondweeds of Africa and Europe than

Fig. 3   *The sea-grass Cymodocea (Thalassodendron) ciliata*

to the true grasses. But the name will do, as it has the merit of indicating that the species (there are several) are not seaweeds or algae.

It is always a puzzle to me that the extensive *Cymodocea* meadows are not exploited by fish much more than they appear to be. They are occasionally nibbled at by several species; I suspect that the bite out of the leaf is more for the epiphyte or small crustacean or coelenterate residing on the leaf than for the leaf itself. They are not grazed or cropped, and I cannot believe that nature has by design allowed so rich a pasture to go unutilized. Perhaps in centuries gone by, before the advent of man the predator, vast herds of Dugong or Dugong-like mammals grazed the meadows. But, they are not used to anything like their potential by fish.

Cheilio inermis and a few other species of Wrasse, such as *Halichoeres* and *Cheilinus,* are indeed found in the meadows and more rarely elsewhere. A few members of the Cardinal fish family (Apogonidae), notably *Apogon nigripes*; the atypical Parrotfish, *Leptoscarus vaigiensis*; and Rabbitfish *Siganus oramin* are more frequently encountered in or near the meadows, but with these few exceptions they do not seem to be a preferred habitat. Several species of sea urchin, on the other hand, live in the seagrass meadows where they often occur in vast multitudes.

3) Extensive areas of coral rubble and rocky debris are often found immediately inshore of the reef platform, where they are deposited by wave action over the outer reef, but they are not confined to this zone. These areas are wealthier in both numbers of different species of fish and in populations of certain species. For example, they form ideal situations for Moray Eels (Muraenidae), many of which are unnoticed by unobservant gogglers. Two species of Damselfish, *Abudefduf annulatus* and *Abudefduf xanthozonus* are more frequently encountered among rubble, where they exercise their territorial imperatives. The Surgeon Fishes (Acanthuridae) are represented by *Acanthurus triostegus*; Apogons, Wrasses, several other species of Damselfish, the aberrant Angelfish *Centropyge multispinis,* and Scorpaenids (including Stonefish) are among the frequently observed species in this habitat. Sea urchins also abound among the rubble, particularly the long-spined Hat-Pin Sea urchin, *Diadema setosa*; sometimes, safe among its spines, are small parties of Apogons and Razorfish.

4) Isolated rocky outcrops and coral heads, often of considerable size, may occur in deeper areas of the lagoon. It is here that quite extraordinary concentrations of many different species are to be found. The protection afforded by isolated rocks and coral heads is at an absolute premium, and the fishwatcher does well to make for these at the earliest opportunity the outgoing tide presents. A catalogue of species likely to be encountered is of little point, as any one of the majority of species described in this book is equally likely to be seen at one time or another.

5) Where there is deeper water of substantial extent in the lagoon, more or less extensive coral gardens may occur. This is the climax habitat, and is richest in species and in densities of species.

6) The reef platform is uncovered at low tides. During spring tides, more extensive areas are bared, when tidal pools are evident. Some of these are surprisingly large, and a system of inter-connected pools is often of sufficient interest and extent to keep an interested goggler enthralled (and submerged) for a full period of low tide. These reef pools abound in animal and plant life, and their walls are thickly encrusted with algae, sponges, bryozoans, tunicates and small corals. They also support dense populations of fish, both resident and those left behind by the receding tide. It would again be tedious to list species, but the pools provide the best possible introduction to many families, especially the Wrasses, Damsels, Surgeons, Soldiers, Rock Cods, Blennies, Scorpions, Boxfish, and a host of others. The pools also have the great advantage of quiet, clear, warm water, and of safety.

7) The lagoon also provides conditions for several rather more specialised habitats. Giant sea anemones are fairly common, even abundant in places, in deeper water, and it is among the tentacles of these that the Anemone fish are to be found. The surface waters are generally calm, and shoals of Halfbeaks and Garfish are often seen. These more tranquil waters are also greatly preferred by the weaker swimmers, such as the Puffers, Boxfish, Cowfish and a host of smaller species.

8) Finally, only for the experienced and the less nervous, the reef slope offers an exciting area of exploration. In addition to most of the species described, the larger sea-going predators will be constant company. For myself, much as I enjoy an occasional visit to the wilder reef slope, the quieter waters of the lagoon and the less exposed corals of inner reef systems are unrivalled in the pleasures they afford.

4 The Fishes: External Form and Description

Fish, like all other animals and plants, carry a scientific name which consists of two Latin or Latinised, less frequently Greek or other, names. This method is known rather grandly as the binomial system of nomenclature, first used on any scale by the Swedish naturalist Carl von Linné (more usually Latinised to Linnaeus) in his book *Systema Naturae* (1735). Linnaeus established order from chaos, simply by classifying the plant and animal worlds logically, into species, genera (singular, genus), families, orders, and so on.

The basic unit of classification is the species; a number of closely related species form the genus. The first of the pair of names denotes the genus, the second is the specific (or species) name. Thus, in *Pterois volitans* (Scorpionfish), *Pterois* indicates the genus, *volitans* the species; *Pterois radiata* is of the same genus, and is a closely related or allied species. Related genera are placed in a family, which ends in the suffix **-idae.**

In addition, in scientific descriptions the two-part name of the species is followed by the surname, usually abbreviated, of the person who first described the species: for example, the full citation is *Pterois volitans* Linn., for Linnaeus. Sometimes the surname is in brackets. *Lethrinus harak* (Forsk.) indicates that Forskal first described the species *harak,* but that later critical work showed that the species was more correctly included in the genus *Lethrinus* (and not the one in which Forskal first placed it.)

All these fine points are covered in an internationally agreed set of rules, which also stipulate the desirability of Latin or Latinised names. Latin is a 'dead' language, and as such does not change; it is understood and accepted by scientists regardless of their native tongues.

In spite of this excellent system, a great deal of confusion in the naming of fish species arose during the latter part of the 1700s and the 1800s. The reasons for this are readily understandable, and there are many. Among the more important, before the days of widely-read journals and the efficient circulation of scientific literature, it frequently happened that the same species was described under two or more different names. There is no great difficulty here: when such a mistake is found, the rules indicate

15

clearly that the name given in the first published description takes priority; the names given in any subsequent descriptions are relegated to the status of synonyms. Some fish have no less than four synonyms.

Of far greater seriousness is an inadequate first description. Many of the early descriptions were inadequate, being based on perhaps a single preserved specimen, several months old, often more or less battered, whose distinctive colours and markings had faded. Juveniles were also often described as different species; in an age ignorant of masks and snorkels, or the paraphernalia of modern aquaria, there were no observational means of correlating with certainty differing juvenile and adult forms of the same species. Preserved material also precluded knowledge of the existence of different colour forms in the same species, or the possible variability of a species within itself.

It is perhaps surprising that the confusion was not worse. These few notes will explain why species, genera and even families sometimes (fortunately not frequently) carry different names in different books. The Gaterinidae or Plectorhynchidae are one such example. This is dealt with in the Gaterinidae, p 64.

The classification of fish is also fraught with difficulty. With most groups of animals some attempt is made to arrange families into a more or less 'natural' system, starting with the most primitive ones and ending with those that show more advanced or climactic features. The fishes mostly defy this, and no satisfactory, generally acceptable natural arrangement has yet been made. All classifications are almost entirely hypothetical.

I have followed the arrangement and sequence of families given by Smith and Smith in their *The Fishes of Seychelles,* for no reason other than that this book is the only recent reference available to anyone seriously interested in the fauna of the Western Indian Ocean.

Fig. 4 is a diagram showing the external features of a typical bony fish; it is a composite diagram and not all the features are found in any one fish. In order to follow the descriptions of the various species it is necessary to know the terms given to each feature.

The first dorsal (1), second dorsal (2), caudal (=tail) (3) and anal (4) fins are unpaired; the dorsal and anals function mainly as stabilisers. The pectoral (5) and pelvic (6) fins are paired, and are used, usually in concert, for rapid turning, and for rising or diving.

The dorsal fin may be single, as in the Garfish and Halfbeaks, or may consist of a first and second fin. These may be separate, as in the diagram; the possession of separate dorsals is a useful and immediate recognition mark of several families, such as the Red Mullets and Cardinal fish. When the fins are separate, the first dorsal usually consists of a number of hard bony spines, the second (soft) dorsal of a single spine followed by a series of rays, which are flexible and have distinct joints.

16

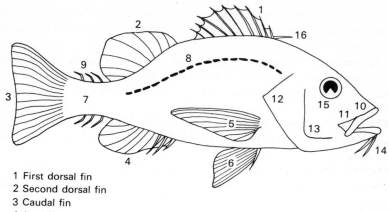

1 First dorsal fin
2 Second dorsal fin
3 Caudal fin
4 Anal fin
5 Pectoral fin
6 Pelvic fin
7 Caudal peduncle
8 Lateral line
9 Finlets
10 Pre-maxilla
11 Maxilla
12 Operculum
13 Pre-opercle
14 Barbels
15 Cheek
16 Horizontal spine before first dorsal fin

Fig. 4 *External features of a bony fish*

In most of the fishes described here, the dorsal fins are confluent and appear as one continuous fin.

The number of spines and rays is either constant or varies within narrow limits for any one species, and is thus a useful character in scientific descriptions. The fin formula is recorded in shorthand: the dorsal fin is abbreviated to D, the number of spines is written in Roman numerals, and the number of rays in Arabic numerals.

Thus, D VII 8 means a continuous dorsal consisting of seven spines and eight rays; D VI+I 5 indicates two separate dorsals, the first of six spines and the second of one spine and five rays. D 16-19 indicates a single dorsal without spines, but with a variable (from sixteen to nineteen) number of rays.

In some species, one or more dorsal spines or rays are greatly elongated or filamentous, as in the pennants of the Moorish Idol and Coachman: these are good field recognition marks.

The dorsal fins in particular are frequently used in displaying: the fin may be folded back in moments of contentment, or erected in aggressive displays.

Counts similar to those for dorsal fins may also be made of the spines and rays in the anal, pectoral and pelvic fins, and thus a complete fin formula, of great help in the diagnosis of species, may be expressed in a single line.

The anal fin usually consists of one to three spines and a number of rays, and is abbreviated to A: A III 7 indicates an anal of three spines and seven rays.

Pectoral fins rarely contain spines; one exception is the Barbel-eel (Plotosidae). They are written as P: P 13 means a pectoral fin of thirteen rays.

Pelvic fins usually have one spine and few (2-5) rays. As the abbreviation P is pre-empted by the pectorals, the shorthand for pelvic fin is V (for ventral fins). V I 5 means a pelvic of one spine and five rays.

Fin spines and rays are normally easy to count, but they require a fish out of water. It is as well to use a short knitting needle as an aid. In several species the dorsal fin spines are grooved and are associated with venom glands: the use of a needle (or matchstick) greatly reduces the chances of being pricked.

The caudal (or tail) fin, which functions mainly as a rudder, does not carry spines. The shape of the caudal is often characteristic of a family (or genus or species), and Fig. 5 illustrates the different shapes. The caudal

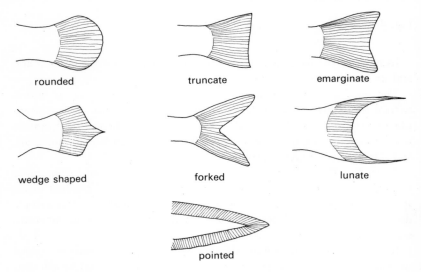

Fig. 5 *Variation in the shape of caudal fins*

fin is usually separate, but may be united to the dorsal and anal fins. Some caudal rays are greatly elongated and filamentous; these are sometimes lost in accidents and are not always a reliable feature in recognition.

Fishes swim by moving their bodies from side to side, and the thrust is mainly derived from the rear part of the body and not the tail fin itself. Eels and eel-like fishes swim with a wave-like motion; in other groups, especially the Triggerfishes, Filefishes, Puffers and Pipefishes, propulsion is achieved by undulatory motions of the dorsal and anal fins.

The caudal peduncle (7) may bear a recognition mark, such as the black or yellow circular spots or bars in several Cardinal fish (Apogonidae); in the Surgeon fishes and Unicorns it carries the scalpels or sharp keels. **The lateral line** (8) is a row of extremely sensitive organs which are linked to the inner ear, and this relays information on currents and turbulence. It is a convenient line along which to count scales; the total number of scales is another useful distinctive character. In addition, the number of rows of scales across the body at the shoulder, expressed as the number above the lateral line and the number below it, is also used in descriptions. These data are again expressed in shorthand: Ll 35 Tr 3/11 means thirty-five scales in the lateral line, and at or near the shoulder there are three rows of scales above the line, and eleven below.

The operculum (12) is a bony flap or cover which protects the gills. One of the bones which makes up the operculum is known as the **pre-opercle** (13), and it is mostly prominent and easily seen. The angle of the pre-opercle sometimes carries a spine, as in the Angelfish (Pomacanthidae) and the Soldier fish (Holocentridae).

Fig. 6 is a diagram of a typical **gill arch,** which carries on its lower side **gill-filaments** and on the upper side **gill-rakers.** The filaments are richly supplied with blood and it is with these that the fish 'breathes'.

The gill-rakers are peg-like processes or projections made of cartilage, and may themselves carry small spines: they are used by some fish as a

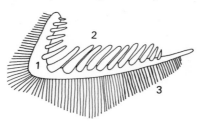

1 Gill-arch
2 Gill-rakers
3 Gill-filaments

Fig. 6 *External features of the gills*

straining or filtering device. The number of gill-rakers, usually those on the lower part of the arch, is reasonably constant for any one species. Where these are prominent and easily counted, their number is another useful measurement to be recorded when describing, comparing or confirming the identity of a species.

Finally, one further set of measurements, of value in species determination, is made routinely by ichthyologists. These are simple measurements, and two of the more important ones are **body depth** and **body length** (or standard length). These are illustrated in Fig. 7. The value for depth is divided into the value for length, and this ratio is expressed simply as 'depth'. If the length of a fish is 20 cm, and the body depth 5 cm, the ratio would appear in a scientific description as 'depth 4'.

The body shape of reef fish is, typically, laterally compressed, or more or less flattened from side to side. In contrast, free-swimming predators usually have a cylindrical or torpedo-shaped body, as in the Barracuda: each shape being adapted to a different way of life. The laterally compressed body is more ideally suited to swimming through narrow interstices or slipping sideways under a low coral or rock. Eel-like or elongated bodies, as in the Morays and Blennies, are adapted to sinuous movements between coral or rock debris and rubble.

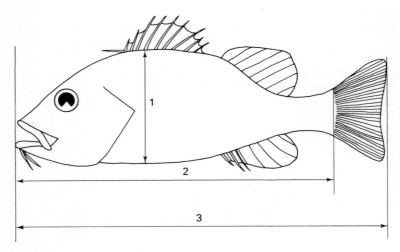

1 Body depth
2 Standard length (or body length)
3 Total length

$$\text{Depth} = \frac{\text{standard length}}{\text{body depth}}$$

Fig. 7 *Dimensions of a fish*

5 The Fishes: Colours, Colour Patterns and Behaviour

Concealment

The most easily understood use of colour or colour patterns is for conceal-ment. The effect of camouflage is perhaps best described as cryptic coloration; in its simplest form the coloration matches the background colour against which the fish habitually lives. The value of concealment to both predators and inoffensive, timid species alike is obvious, and it is an evolutionary end-point which has been successfully achieved by a great multitude of animals.

Cryptic coloration or colour resemblance can be described as protective only in the case of the non-predators. With predators the motive is different, but the adaptive behaviour of both predator and non-predator is the same: because movement is liable to result in detection, cryptically coloured fish tend to lie motionless and are among the least active of the reef community. The Stonefish is perhaps the supreme example of both cryptic coloration and behaviour.

It is not generally appreciated that the possession of silvery sides together with countershading is also an effective means of camouflage. Two different optical principles are concerned with these effects. In countershading, the upper surface of the fish is dark-coloured and the sides are lighter or silver. This counters the normal effects of incident light, which is for the upper surface to be more brightly illuminated, and thus to appear lighter, and the lower surfaces to be less brightly illumin-ated, and to appear darker. The net effect of countershading is thus to render the fish less recognisable.

Because water is illuminated from above, and light is refracted and scattered within it, the eye receives about one hundred times the intensity of light when looking upwards through water as when looking down. When looking horizontally, however, the scattered light is of uniform intensity. If a mirror is held vertically under water it merely reflects light similar in intensity to that which would be received by an eye if the mirror were not there: the mirror is thus essentially 'invisible'. Silvery sides behave like a mirror, and are thus of great value to many free-swimming fish of the reef. The Halfbeaks and the Garfish are good examples of the effective use of countershading and silvery sides.

Advertisement

It is, however, the brilliance of coloration of coral fish that impresses even the most casual of observers. Before attempting an explanation of possible reasons for this outstanding characteristic, I will give a brief generalised account of how the colours are produced.

There are thousands of pigment cells in the skin, called **chromatophores,** which contain either melanin pigments, which give rise basically to black or brown colours, or carotenoid pigments, which give rise to yellows, oranges and reds. The pigments can be expanded or contracted, and thus the colours appear more or less intense or marked. The colours in a fish will depend on the proportions of the two different pigments as well as on their degree of expansion or contraction. For example, yellow and black will appear as these colours when used independently. When they are used in concert, and depending on their arrangement and relative proportions, they may give rise to a variety of shades of green or brown.

In addition to the chromatophores, there are reflecting cells called **iridocytes** which contain, in crystalline form, an excretory product guanine. These reflecting cells increase greatly the range of colours and give the iridescent effects which are so much a feature of coral fish.

Each chromatophore is connected to the nervous system by nerve fibres, and the fish is thus able to a large extent to control and alter the shading and intensity of its colours at will. This can be achieved very quickly: Surgeon fish for example can switch from light to dark brown in a split second; and many fish are able to intensify or extinguish markings in immediate response to a stimulus.

The system allows not only for the development of species with different colours, but of different colour patterns. We must now consider the uses to which these have been put by the reef fish.

Two outstanding characteristics of communities of coral fish are diversity of often closely related species and population densities. In crowded, complex communities, where members are always in very close physical contact, immediate recognition of a species is of very great importance indeed. Recognition is particularly important between closely related species of the same genus, and between closely related genera. The importance is again compounded when species are territorial. Territoriality means the acquisition and occupation of 'private property', and although it is not by any means an absolute rule, those species which exhibit strong aggressive territorial behaviour tend towards bright coloration. With territories crowded one on another, we see a further good reason for the development of bright colours in facilitating immediate recognition between the same species, and between different species.

It seems, then, that one of the more important functions of bright colours or colour patterns is to serve as a conspicuous and unmistakable aid to identity.

In the majority of cases the use of colour as a flag of identity is further strengthened by special patterns or marks. Sometimes these take the form of an ocellus or eye-spot, a circular black or dark-coloured mark, often situated on the flank or posterior end of the soft dorsal. Occasionally the ocellar spots have a brilliant iridescent margin. In other examples, there are one or more vertical or horizontal black bars. This system is used in the Butterfly fish, where many species of *Chaetodon* have an almost identical body shape, are of similar body colour, and are of similar size. Primary recognition marks in this genus consist of variously arranged dark lines and black bars (compare the species on pages 47-52 and Colour Plate 5); secondary recognition marks are provided by fin colour.

It is important for a successful species to prevent or reduce the chances of cross-breeding or hybridisation, and colours and colour-patterns are one of the main means of achieving this end: they serve to stimulate successful meeting and subsequent breeding between male and female of the same species; but they also serve to block any nascent emotional response between males and females of different species.

In summary, colour and colour patterns thus make recognition certain, particularly between closely related species. They preclude chance cross-breeding and so maintain a species in breeding isolation and they amplify the effects of displays in territorial behaviour.

Colour patterns

Colour patterns are also of intrinsic value in serving to disrupt the outline or contour of a fish and this is known as disruptive coloration. As such, colour patterns are used for two entirely different purposes: as recognition aids at short ranges, and as an aid to concealment at longer ranges. Interpretation of an object as likely prey is dependent on recognition of a characteristic outline and body contours. These are most effectively disrupted when a pattern of light and dark lines or stripes cuts across or breaks up the body contour, and are also interrupted abruptly at the margins of the body outline. This serves if not to prevent recognition, at least to delay it. The Emperor Angelfish (*Pomacanthodes imperator*) is a good example of disruptive coloration: at short range the fish is most conspicuous, but at any distance the body contours and outline are remarkably effectively broken by light and dark areas and stripes.

The correlation between complex, crowded communities and brilliant coloration of their constituent species seems also to hold good in at least one other totally different environment. In the freshwater lakes of the Rift Valley system of Eastern Africa, especially in Lake Tanganyika and Lake Malawi, a single family of fish, the Cichlidae, has evolved in an explosion of closely related species. Cichlids are well-known to freshwater aquarium enthusiasts through popular and colourful South American species such as the Angelfish (*Pterophyllum*), the Jack Dempsey (*Cichlasoma*) and many others; African Cichlids are equally attractive, but not widely known.

In the Rift Valley Lakes, Cichlid communities are also complex and crowded, and here, too, many species are remarkable for the brilliance of their colours. The Cichlids have solved the acute problems of recognition in the same way, exploiting the potentialities of colour and colour patterns.

Behaviour

There are two very different behavioural patterns of reef fish which are of interest. While many species are solitary, others are social, and occur in shoals, often of a vast size. Between these two extremes, there is a range of social patterns, most of which may be found among the Damselfish (Pomacentridae).

Solitary species tend towards strong territorial behaviour, and they defend their territories aggressively. Aggressive displays are usually strongest at the centre of the territory, or home area, and aggression decreases with distance from the 'home'. While aggression is most viciously directed against individuals of the same species, this is not always so, and many Pomacentrids will attack a human hand or foot when these approach the territory. Several species of *Abudefduf* do this; so do the Anemone fish (*Amphiprion*), leaving their Giant Sea Anemone home to display aggressively.

Solitary species pair during breeding; in some a more or less permanent pair-bond has developed and here the male and female are jointly aggressive. Yet other species live in shoals which occupy a 'group' territory; *Dascyllus aruanus* does this, a social group occupying a stagshorn coral.

Then there are the truly social species which shoal. Shoaling is a most interesting behavioural pattern; it occurs generally in the larval and very young of many species, and in some it persists through to adulthood and life. There are several advantages to be gained from the shoaling habit. The earliest recognised advantage, and one which has been much debated and contested, is that of mutual protection from predators. It has been shown that a predator meets with most success when presented with a single object of prey. As more objects of prey are presented, and especially if these are moving rapidly and erratically, the number of successful strikes by the predator decreases. This is known as the 'confusion' effect, the predator being presented with numerous conflicting stimuli, which results in confusion. There are other advantages. While a shoal is conspicuous, the grouping of individuals affords less chance of a predator-prey meeting than if the individual fish were widely scattered at random over a large area. Again, because range of sight in water is relatively short, a compact, dense shoal will appear, from any distance, as a large and substantial object, which may well act as a deterrent. Finally, it is probable that a shoal will locate food for the group benefit more efficiently than individuals of the same species acting independently.

Shoals of many species of reef fish behave with incredible co-ordination and precision. The highly sensitive lateral line must obviously play an important role here; but colour, colour patterns and shoaling marks are also of value. Many shoaling species have conspicuous horizontal or vertical lines, stripes or bars, or spots on flanks or fins. These serve the all-important function of communication between members of the shoal, yet another use of colour and colour patterns.

Finally, there are a number of specialised uses of colour advertisement. The simplest of these is the use of gaudy colours or colour patterns to advertise distastefulness, poisonous properties or the possession of an acutely venomous weaponry of spines. This warning coloration is well developed in Pufferfishes and Boxfishes and in some species of Scorpion-fishes, notably *Pterois*; in general they are left severely alone by all predators. As a further aid to their inedibility, the Puffers are able to inflate themselves with air or water, rendering themselves even more conspicuous and using this as a threat display. In consequence, the behaviour of these fish is anything but timid; they have an insolent boldness about them and go about their business quite unconcernedly.

Mimicry is a very specialised use of colour, where the coloration of a more or less edible species mimics the colour of a highly poisonous or otherwise distasteful species, or of species otherwise generally immune to predation. For example, a species of Filefish has mimicked a Pufferfish; and a species of Blenny has used the Cleaner Wrasse as a model. Both species are discussed in more detail in the relevant descriptions.

The use of red coloration, used by all common species of Soldier fish (Holocentridae), is also rather more specialised in function. Red is virtually invisible underwater at night, and here the species, all predators, are adapted to nocturnal feeding. By day they are extremely wary, hiding under coral or rock overhangs.

Of particular interest is the disruptive pattern of the eye-stripe, used for effectively camouflaging the eye. Here, the black pupil of the eye is included in a black bar or stripe which runs across the face, and the eye is thus concealed. Deception is sometimes carried a stage further by a prominent eye-spot or ocellus situated towards the rear of the fish, often on the posterior of the dorsal fin. The lunge of the striking predator is made towards the ocellus; the possessor of which does not have to execute a possibly fatal turn before rapid flight.

Plate 1

1 *Synodus variegatus* p.29
2 *Holocentrus spiniferus* p.30
3 *Holocentrus sammara* p.30
4 *Myripristis murdjan* p.31

Plate 2

1

2

3

4

1 *Paracirrhites forsteri* p.34
2 *Cephalopholis argus* p.36
3 *Epinephelus merra* p.36
4 *Anthias squamipinnis* p.38

Plate 3

1 *Ostorhinchus fleurieu* p.38
2 *Paramia quinquelineata* p.39
3 *Gnathanodon speciosus* p.40
4 *Platax pinnatus* p.42

Plate 4

1
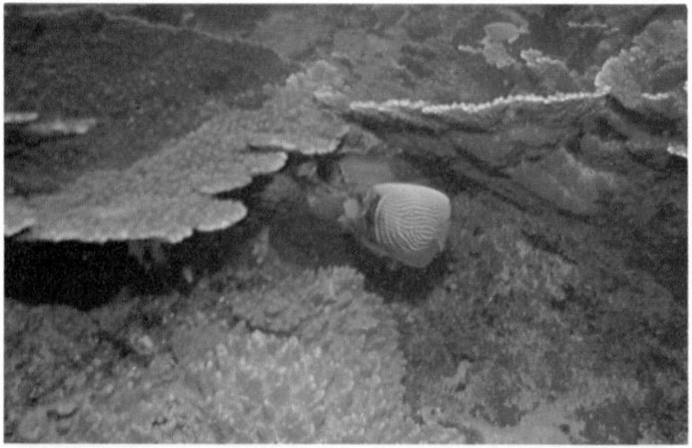

2
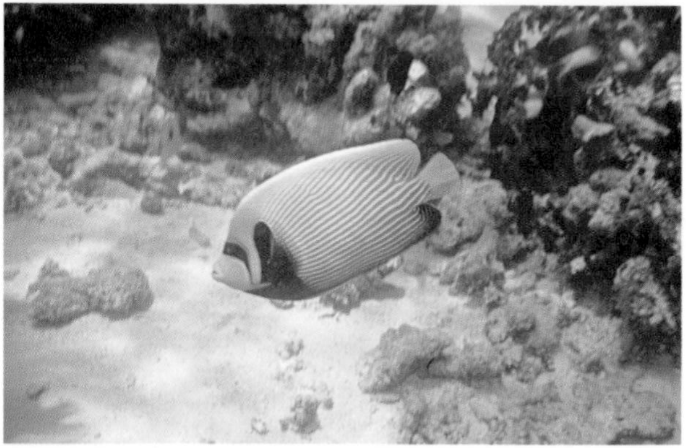

3
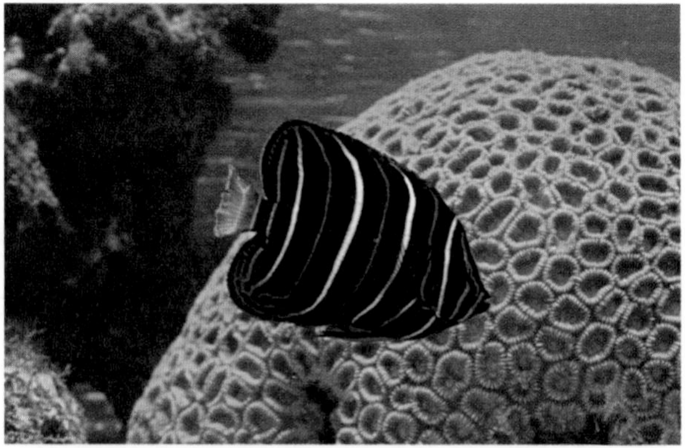

4
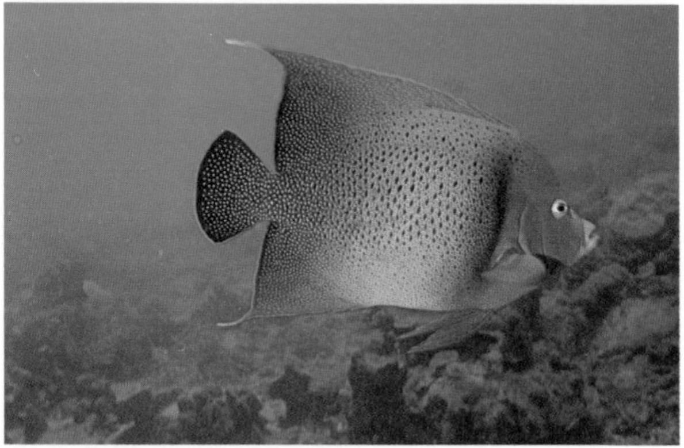

1 *Pomacanthodes imperator (juvenile)* p.44

3 *Pomacanthops semicirculatus (juvenile)* p.44

1 *Pomacanthodes chrysurus* p.44
2 *Chaetodon auriga* and *Chaetodon lunula* p.46 and p.47
3 *Chaetodon trifasciatus* p.47
4 *Chaetodon melanotus* p.47

Plate 6

1 *Heniochus acuminatus* p.51

3 *Acanthurus leucosternon and Acanthurus triostegus* p.53

Plate 7

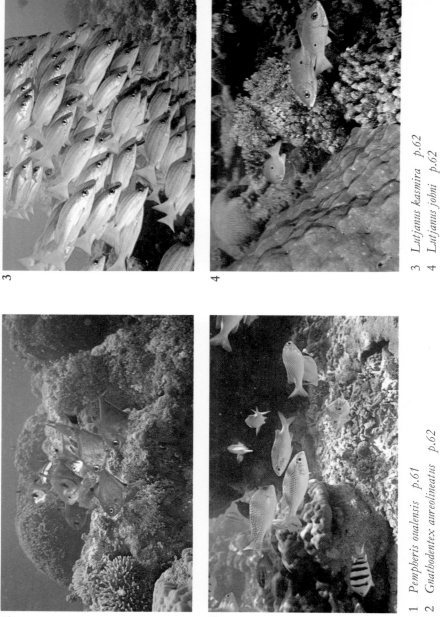

1 *Pempheris oualensis* p.61
2 *Gnathodentex aureolineatus* p.62
3 *Lutjanus kasmira* p.62
4 *Lutjanus jobmi* p.62

Plate 8

1
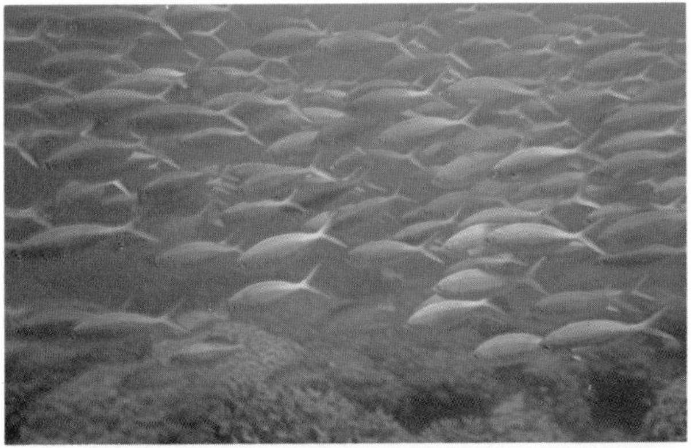

2
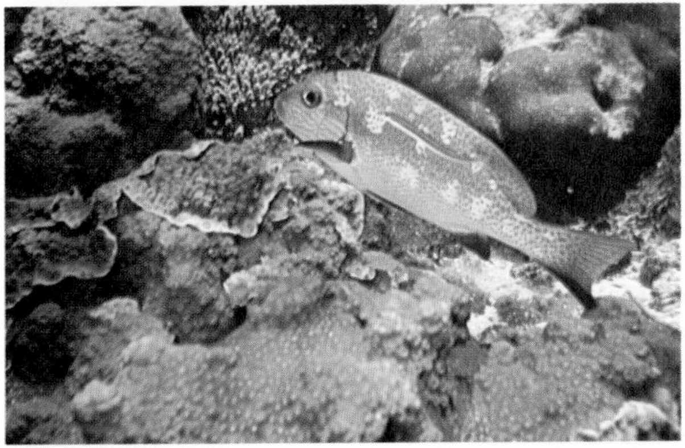

3
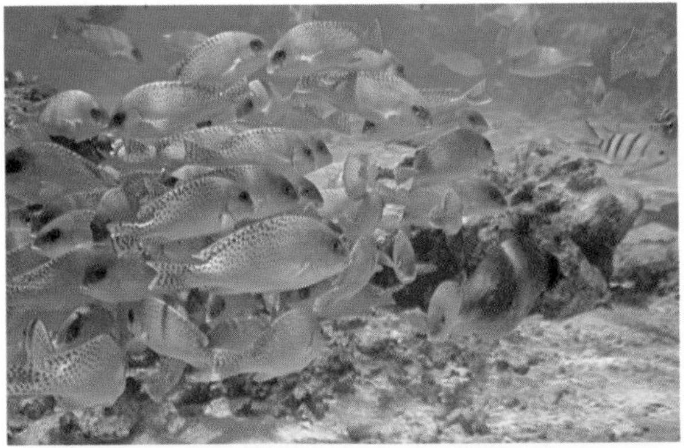

4
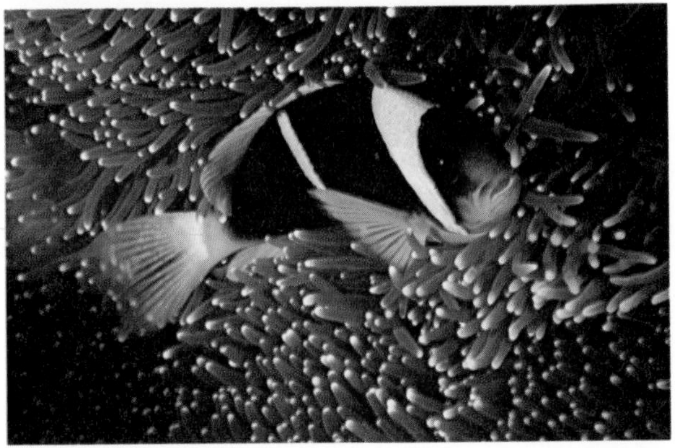

1 *Caesio xanthonotus* p.64
2 *Gaterin flavomaculatus* p.65
3 *Gaterin gaterinus* p.65
4 *Amphiprion ephippium* p.69

Plate 9

1   *Amphiprion akallopisos*   p.69
2   *Abudefduf sexfasciatus*   p.69
3   *Abudefduf dicki*   p.69
4   *Abudefduf saxatilis*   p.69

Plate 10

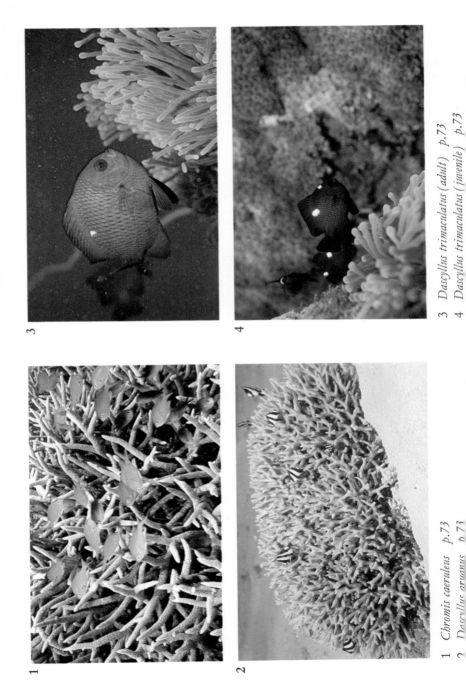

1 *Chromis caeruleus* p.73
2 *Dascyllus aruanus* p.73
3 *Dascyllus trimaculatus (adult)* p.73
4 *Dascyllus trimaculatus (juvenile)* p.73

Plate 11

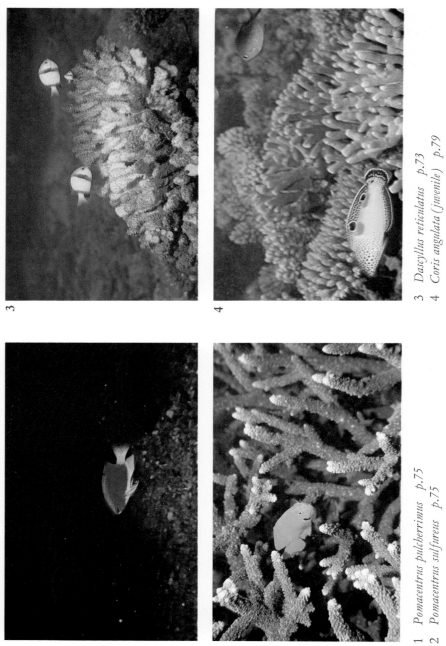

1   *Pomacentrus pulcherrimus*   p.75
2   *Pomacentrus sulfureus*   p.75
3   *Dascyllus reticulatus*   p.73
4   *Coris angulata (juvenile)*   p.79

Plate 12

1
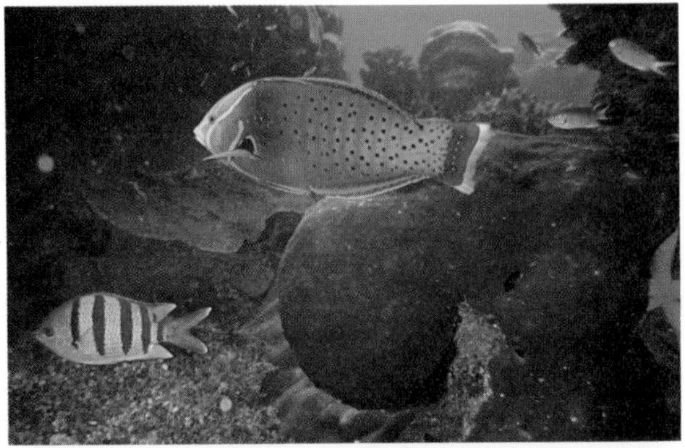

2
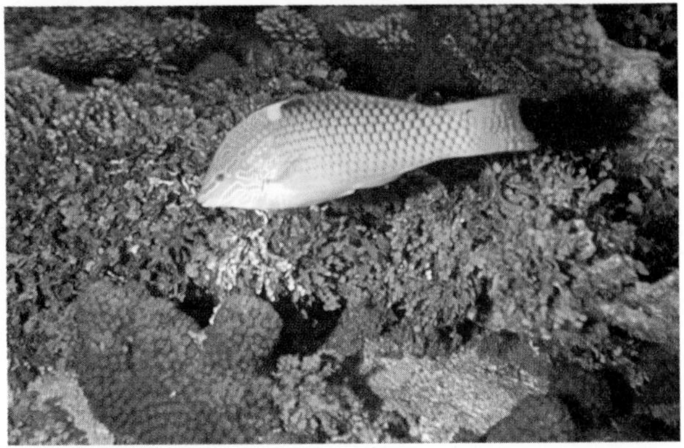

3
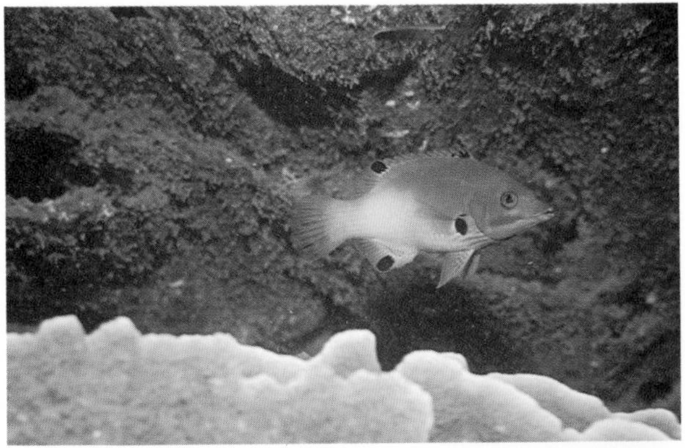

4
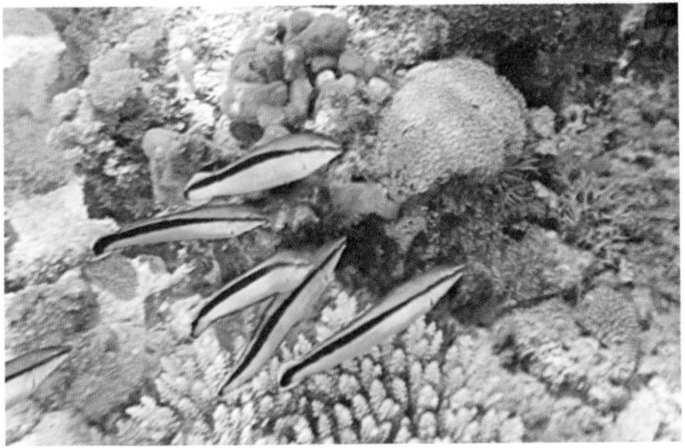

1 *Coris formosa (adult)* p.79
2 *Halichoeres centriquadrus* p.78

3 *Lepidaplois axillaris* p.79
4 *Labroides dimidiatus* p.77

Plate 13

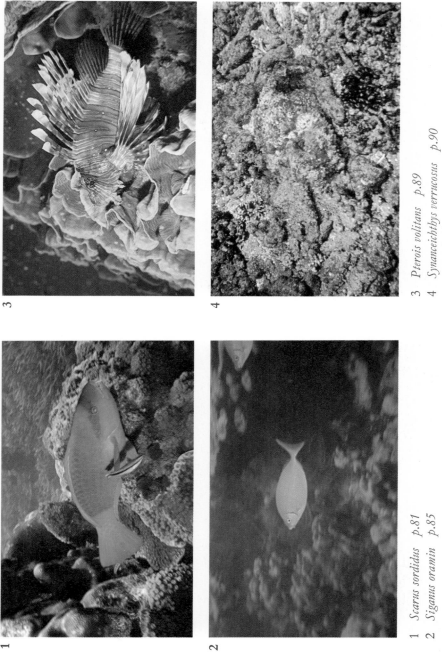

1   *Scarus sordidus*   *p.81*
2   *Siganus oramin*   *p.85*

3   *Pterois volitans*   *p.89*
4   *Synanceichthys verrucosus*   *p.90*

Plate 14

1   *Lycodontis favagineus*   *p.93*
2   *Balistapus undulatus*   *p.94*

3   *Rhinecanthus aculeatus*   *p.94*
4   *Oxymonacanthus longirostris*   *p.95*

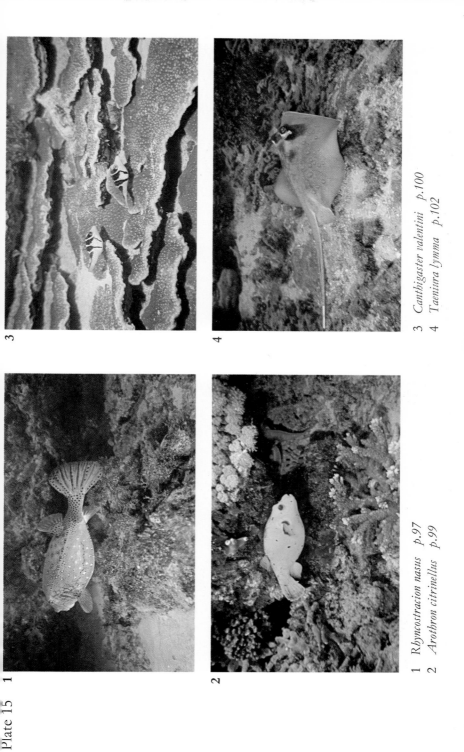

Plate 15

3

4

1

2

1 Rhyncostracion nasus p.97
2 Arothron citrinellus p.99
3 Canthigaster valentini p.100
4 Taeniura lymma p.102

Plate 16

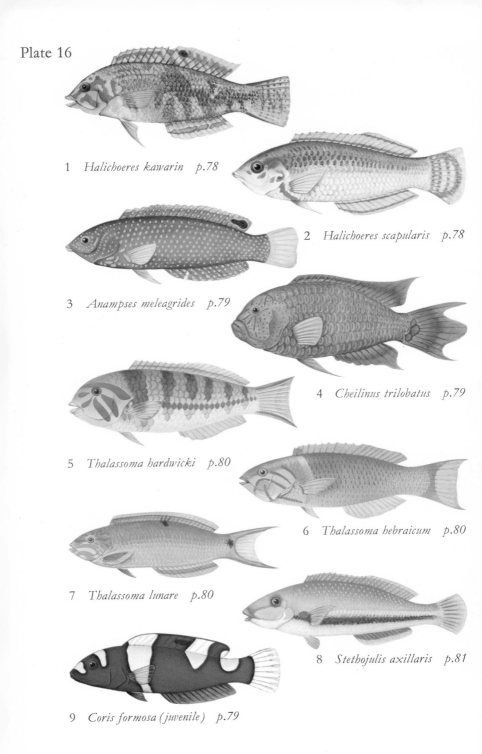

1 *Halichoeres kawarin* p.78

2 *Halichoeres scapularis* p.78

3 *Anampses meleagrides* p.79

4 *Cheilinus trilobatus* p.79

5 *Thalassoma hardwicki* p.80

6 *Thalassoma hebraicum* p.80

7 *Thalassoma lunare* p.80

8 *Stethojulis axillaris* p.81

9 *Coris formosa (juvenile)* p.79

6 The Fishes: Descriptions of the Common Species

Common names Wherever possible, I have included the common names of the fishes. The abbreviations are 'S' for Swahili, 'Sey' for Seychellois, and 'Q' for the names used in Queensland, Australia.

Fish lengths Although it is more usual in scientific papers to express lengths in millimetres, I have given them in centimetres throughout. The lengths are an indication of the size attained by average adult specimens, and do not constitute records.

Formulae I have included fin and other measurements (see Chapter Four) for most but not all species. With some species they are unnecessary (for example, the Moray Eels, where other measurements which have not been described are made); with others I have been unable to find a reliable source of reference. Most measurements have been taken from J.L.B. Smith's *Fishes of Southern Africa* or from his numerous Ichthyological Bulletins; the remainder are from equally reliable published sources.

Descriptions I have kept these brief, particularly where there are coloured photographs or drawings. Only those characters which are likely to be of most use in field identification have been included. Shape is all-important, then colour, and then conspicuous marks.

CLUPEIDAE and ENGRAULIDAE: Sardines and Anchovies; Simu, Dagaa (S)

Sardines and Anchovies occur in shoals in shallow water in most localities along the coast throughout the year. Sardines, in particular, appear seasonally in vast shoals (usually between December and February in Eastern Africa). They are mostly small, silvery fish with a single dorsal fin, forked tails, and with scales that are easily shed. Identification of species is at best difficult.

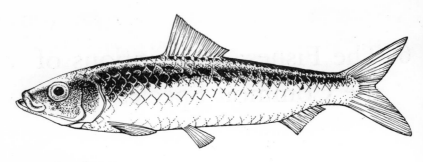

Sardinella melaneura

Sardinella melaneura 15 cm. Sardine, Simu (S), Sardine de France (Sey). Sides of body silvery, back and upper parts olive-green to bluish, with a pale yellow line between. No lateral line; scales very easily shed; mouth large, with no teeth. D 15-16; A 18-19; Tr 11; 34-45 gill-rakers; Depth 4.0.

PLOTOSIDAE: Barbel-eels; Ngogo, Tondi (S)

A large family of fish, most of the 1,000 species of 'Catfish' or Barbel-eels live in fresh water. They all have one or more pairs of sensory feelers or barbels around the mouth; their bodies are eel-like and mostly taper to a point. There is only one common species in our area.

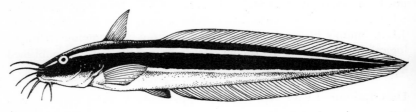

Plotosus arab

Plotosus arab 45 cm. Barbel-eel, Ngogo (S), Machoiron (Sey).
Juveniles as illustrated above; adults, greyish or brownish, only rarely encountered. Juveniles common to abundant, in dense, compact shoals in creek or lagoon shallows: colour black, with two horizontal white or cream lines. There are four pairs of barbels; body without scales. The single dorsal fin and pectorals each have one **sharp serrated spine, which may inflict most painful wounds.** For this reason even small Barbel-eels should be treated with some caution. Shoals often excavate a hole in the sand, usually under or near a rock. D I 5; total D+A rays less than 200; 22-24 gill-rakers; no scales; Depth about 7.0.

SYNODIDAE: Lizard fishes; Goromwe (S); Grinners (Q)

Lizard fishes apparently derive their common name from the shape of the head. They are predators, and have large mouths with sharp teeth. In certain areas they are economically important, as in the Ganges estuary where the local species is dried and marketed as Bombay Duck. The Queensland name is remarkably apt, as when about to strike, the mouth of *Synodus* is opened in a ghastly carnivorous grin.

Synodus variegatus 30 cm. Lizard fish.
See Colour Plate 1, No 1; body cylindrical, with scales; colour brownish but apparently variable at will, from lighter (when lying on sand) to darker (when on rock), but always with a number of dark blotches evident. Common in all localities, usually solitary, lizard fish lie motionless in wait for their prey: when the victim is almost vertically above, they dart upwards and seize it. No apparent preference of species for food. D 11-13; A 8-10; L.l. 58-62; P 12-13; Depth 6.0-7.0.

HEMIRAMPHIDAE: Halfbeaks; Chuchungi (S); Garfish (Q)

The lower jaw only of the Halfbeaks is elongated into a bony beak. These fish inhabit the surface waters of lagoons and creeks, and are able, when pursued, to make a series of hops out of the water. The lower lobe of the caudal fin beats very rapidly from side to side, and this impetus, aided by extended pectorals, enables the fish to cover modest distances along the surface. Halfbeaks are closely related to flying fish; in the latter the pectoral fins are greatly enlarged and assist the fish to glide for appreciable distances after breaking surface.

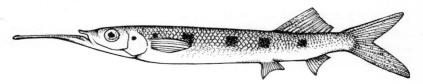

Hemiramphus far

Hemiramphus far 40 cm. Halfbeak.
Easily recognised, body green-blue above, silvery on sides and below, about 6 or 7 black bars as indicated. In shoals, just below surface only; they feed mainly on shrimp-like and other small crustacea. Common in lagoons and creeks. D 13-14; A 10-13; L.l. about 56; Depth 6.0-8.0.

BELONIDAE: Garfishes; Mtumbu (S); Aiguille (Sey); Long Toms (Q)

Fierce and swift predators of surface waters, Garfishes have elongated, sub-cylindrical bodies with elongated jaws, equipped with a formidable array of sharp teeth. The flesh is good eating, but the bones are bright green. For some curious, confusing reason they are known as Long Toms in Australia, while the Halfbeaks are called Garfish there.

Tylosurus crocodilus

Tylosurus crocodilus 150 cm. Garfish.
Easily recognised, body elongated, blue-green above, silver below; dorsal and anal fins set well back, near the forked caudal. An unmistakable fish; common in surface of lagoons and creeks. D 22-23; A 19-21; Depth about 15.0.

HOLOCENTRIDAE: Soldier fishes; Vifuvu (S); Lion (Sey)

Soldier fishes are all brilliantly red or orange-bronze coloured; and they are mostly wary, hiding under covered crevices or overhangs in living coral or rocks. Their red colour and large eyes suggest they are mainly nocturnal; they are never observed feeding during daylight hours. Soldier fish are considered to be a fairly primitive group, the extremely spiny nature of the fins being cited as an indication of this. There are two genera in our area, *Holocentrus* and *Myripristis*. These are readily distinguishable by their shape (see Colour Plate 1 and compare illustrations 2 and 3 with 4); *Holocentrus* has a strong opercular spine, while *Myripristis* has not.

Holocentrus spiniferus 45 cm. Scarlet-fin Soldier fish (Q).
See Colour Plate 1, No 2; first dorsal scarlet, other fins yellow to orange. Crimson spot behind eye, another at pectoral axil. About coral, wary.

Holocentrus sammara 30 cm.
See Colour Plate 1, No 3; brownish red, with bronzy horizontal lines; black blotch on front of dorsal fin; small reddish dots on chin and chest. The behaviour of this species does not entirely conform to that of most

others: though wary, it is more venturesome and is often encountered away from protective cover. D XI 11-12; A IV 7-8; L.l. 38-44; Tr 3/7; Depth about 3.5.

Allied species:

Holocentrus diadema 30 cm. Lion Parasol (Sey).
Not illustrated; red with horizontal light (whitish) stripes; dorsal fin blotched black; strong anal spines. Under coral overhangs (plate coral is often favoured), or in crevices and holes; very wary. D XI-XII 12-13; A IV 8-9; L.l. 46-48; Tr 3/8; Depth about 3.3.

Myripristis murdjan 30 cm. Lion Gros Yeux (Sey).
See Colour Plate 1, No 4; the large eyes, deeper body and forked tail preclude confusion with *Holocentrus*. A very common species; wary. D XI 13-15; A IV 12-14; L.l. 28-30; Tr 3/7; Depth about 2.8.

Allied species:

Myripristis pralinius 20 cm.
Not illustrated; easily confused with *murdjan*: red coloration is similar, and both have a darkish to black bar at rear of operculum; this bar tends to be more extensive in *pralinius*. *M. murdjan* has a black area at rear edge of dorsal and anal fins and at caudal tips, *pralinius* does not. Common.

Myripristis adustus 25 cm.
Not illustrated; similar to both preceding species, but differs in having second dorsal, caudal and anal fins white; edged with dark brown. Common. Wary.

SOLEIDAE: Flatfish; Wayo (S)

There are several species of flatfish in our area, but all except one inhabit deeper and often more turbid water and are rarely encountered in the shallow lagoons. They all start life as normal looking fish, but soon either the left or the right eye migrates across the head, and the fish then lies either on its left or right side. (This is constant for any related species and is a characteristic used in their classification.) Flatfish are predators. To assist them in this they are experts at concealment and are able to darken, lighten or mottle their body colour to match the background.

Pardachirus marmoratus 25 cm. Flatfish.
Not illustrated; colour variable, always light (whitish) on sand; dark-spotted, with four or five blobs of gold in a line along the middle of the

fish. These gold spots are an unmistakable recognition mark. The fish often half-buries itself in the sand and then its outline is barely discernible. It will stand its ground nervously and will swim off at surprising speed at the last moment. It occurs throughout the area in suitable sandy lagoonal and creek habitats, but it is nowhere abundant. D 67; A 53; L.l. 100.

SYNGNATHIDAE: Pipefishes and Seahorses

The Pipefishes and Seahorses are well known and are scarcely in need of introduction; their body shapes are unmistakable. While Pipefish are abundant in all suitable localities, Seahorses *Hippocampus* must be considered uncommon as they are seen only very infrequently. The family shows parental care, but it is the male which attaches the eggs to a brood pouch situated on its belly (Seahorses) or tail (Pipefishes). All species have small mouths at the end of tube-like snouts, a characteristic they share with the related Flutemouths and Razorfishes.

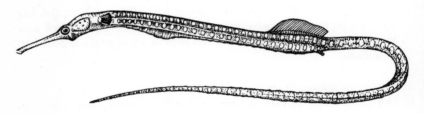

Yozia bicoarctata

Yozia bicoarctata 38 cm. Pipefish.
Body colour pale buffish to sandy; small brown spots on head and body. Habitat preference sandy areas, or open eroded rocky coral platforms in shallows, or among smaller coral debris.

Allied species:
    Doryramphus melanopleura 8 cm.
    Not illustrated; is a bright horizontally striped red and blue pipefish with a comparatively large flat angular tail. Infrequently seen, but widespread.
    Hippocampus sp., probably *kuda,* the Seahorse.
    Not illustrated; is presumably locally common, but is rarely observed off the Kenya Coast.

AULOSTOMIDAE: Trumpet fishes

Long-bodied, with an elongated tubular snout; first dorsal consists of a series of separate small triangular spines; second dorsal and anal fins equal or sub-equal and set far back. Only one species in our area.

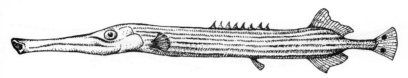

Aulostomus valentini

Aulostomus valentini 60 cm. Trumpet fish, Trompette (Sey).
Unmistakable; description and characteristics as for family. Body colour greyish, but variable. Wary, in lagoons or creeks, never far from protective cover. Usually solitary, never abundant, but present throughout area. D VIII-XII+24-27; A 22-25; no gill-rakers.

FISTULARIDAE: Flutemouths; Shaukwani (S)

Very long bodies, depressed, so that the body is wider than deep; elongated tubular snout. Dorsal and anal fins equal, set far back. Diagnostic feature long, filamentous mid-caudal rays. There is only one species in our area.

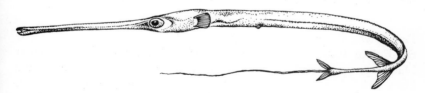

Fistularia petimba

Fistularia petimba 180 cm. Flutemouth.
Unmistakable; body colour darkish green to greenish brown above, lighter below. Interrupted blue stripes from head to tail; fins occasionally orange. In twos and threes. Movement surprisingly swift when pursued. Common in shallows. Carnivorous, feeding on small fish. D 14-17; A 14-16.

CENTRISCIDAE: Razorfishes

Laterally very compressed, body deepish, narrowing to a razor-edge on belly. Spine at rear of body is first dorsal spine; remainder of dorsal fin and caudal are displaced to underside of body. Unmistakable.

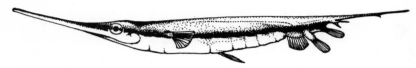

Aeoliscus strigatus

Aeoliscus strigatus 15 cm. Razorfish, Canif (Sey).
Body colour dark above, lighter beneath, with one broadish black horizontal bar from snout, through eye, to spine. Long tubular snout. These fish swim head-down. They usually occur in small shoals; when approached, they turn so that their thinnest dimension is presented. Often found among sea-urchin spines or between fish-trap stakes. Widespread, but nowhere abundant.

CIRRHITIDAE: Hawkfishes

Small (to 25 cm) often brightly coloured carnivorous fish with more or less truncate, never forked, tails. Solitary, probably territorial, individuals lie motionless on top of coral or a rock.

Paracirrhites forsteri 25 cm.
See Colour Plate 2, No 1; multi-coloured: head, gill-covers and chest blue-grey, upper half of body light yellow-orange, then a horizontal black stripe from dorsal to caudal. Front third with pronounced spots. Common throughout our area, but never abundant. D X 11; A III 6; L.l. about 50; Tr 5/11; Depth about 3.0.

Allied species:
Cirrhitichthys oxycephalus 10 cm.
Not illustrated; body colour whitish, with numerous reddish brown irregular blotches; tips of dorsal fin spines with clusters of very short, red hair-like filaments. Among coral. Common, never abundant. D X 12; A III 6; L.l. about 40; Tr 4/12; Depth about 2.5.

TERAPONIDAE: Jarbuas, Thornheads; Ngagu (S)

Small silvery fishes which are found in rocky shoreline pools or shallows, mostly bearing conspicuous horizontal black stripes as a series of arcs along body.

Therapon jarbua

Therapon jarbua 30 cm. Jarbua, Ngagu or Tende (S), Peau d'Ane (Sey), Crescent Perch (Q).
Silver, with three black arcs along body. Operculum with spines; first dorsal strongly spiny. Common in rocky shoreline tidal pools, or in shallows with rocky bottoms. D XI-XII 10-11; A III 7-9; L.l. about 80; Tr 14/24; 13-14 gill-rakers; Depth about 3.0.

SERRANIDAE: Rock Cods, Groupers; Tewa (S); Vieille (Sey).

Robust-bodied fish with large mouths and of fairly constant body shape; caudal fin rounded or truncate, never forked. Many species in our area, probably at least thirty, but most inhabit deeper water. Most species hide under coral overhangs and rocks at low tide. Solitary and territorial, Rock Cods do not take flight readily, preferring to bluff it out; they are thus comparatively easily speared. For this reason they are vulnerable to over-exploitation and it is likely that populations of several species are already seriously depleted. They are certainly more in evidence in areas such as Marine Parks and Reserves where they are protected.

Several species grow to a considerable size (360 cm) and attain weights of several hundred kilograms, and these giants are sometimes encountered in surprisingly shallow water (5 metres). They are dangerous and should not be provoked under any circumstances.

Cephalopholis argus 30 cm. Blue-spotted Rock Cod, Tewa, Tewa Shambaru (S), Vieille Cecille (Sey).
See Colour Plate 2, No 2; body colour brownish (variable) with many bright blue spots; unmistakable. Frequently encountered in deeper lagoonal waters around rocks and coral; one of the more consistently seen species, but nowhere abundant. D IX 15-17; A III 8-9; 9 gill-rakers; Depth about 2.8.

Allied species:
> *Cephalopholis miniatus* 30 cm. Coral Trout, Tewa Ndudu (S), Vieille Anana (Sey).
> Not illustrated; body colour brilliant red, with bright blue spots. Deeper water only.

Epinephelus merra 60 cm. Honeycomb Rock Cod, Tewa Chui (S).
See Colour Plate 2, No 3; markings more or less hexagonal, giving a honeycomb effect. Dorsal, anal and caudal fins spotted. Solitary; common in all areas where coral, coral debris or rocks provide protective cover. D XI 15-17; A III 8; 15-17 gill-rakers; Depth about 3.0.

Allied species:
> *Epinephelus macrospilos* 44 cm.
> Not illustrated; may be confused with *E. merra,* but is readily distinguished by having rounder, not angular, spots, and a few large irregular blotches (not spots) on dorsal and caudal fins. Formula as for *merra,* but gill-rakers 11 plus 5 anterior knobs.
> *Epinephelus tauvina* 180 cm. Estuary Rock Cod (Q).
> Not illustrated; sub-adult colour whitish to greyish white, with few large irregularly-shaped dark brown blotches; body with numerous small red spots. Adults uniform dark brown, spots indistinct. Individuals 30-80 cm seen in rocky shallows; large adults possibly dangerous. D XI 15-16; A III 8; 9-11 gill-rakers plus several rudiments; Depth 3.3.

Grammistes sexlineatus 23 cm. Vieille Plate Canal (Sey).
The smallest of the Rock Cods. Colour black or brownish black, with 4-5 creamy to pale yellow horizontal lines. Found only under protective cover in holes in rock or coral: extremely wary. The body is coated with a thick layer of mucus; this may be toxic to other fishes in the confines of small aquaria. Common in suitable localities (especially shallow lagoons) throughout the area. D VI-VII 13-15; A 8-11; 7-9 prominent gill-rakers; Depth about 2.5.

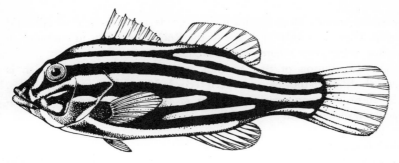

Grammistes sexlineatus

Other species:

> *Pomicrops lanceolatus* 360 cm. Rock Cod, Grouper, Tewa Mziswe (S).
> Not illustrated; attains great size, then possibly dangerous if provoked.
> Young golden-yellow, with broadish dark bands; adults uniform
> brown or blackish, fins yellowish. D XI 14-15; A III 8; Tr 14/45;
> 14 gill-rakers. Depth about 3.0.
> *Variola louti* 120 cm. Kopwi (S), Vroissant (Sey), Lunar-tailed Rock
> Cod (Q).
> Not illustrated; body colour reddish brown, with very numerous
> small lilac or purple spots; fins edged yellow; caudal markedly lunate,
> not rounded. This fish forms a link between the Rock Cods and the
> Jewelfishes. D IX 13-14; A III 8; Tr 15/50; gill-rakers mere knobs;
> Depth about 3.0.

ANTHIIDAE: Jewelfishes

The Jewelfishes are so closely related to the Rock Cods (Serranidae) that
they are usually included in that family, but are given sub-family status,
the Anthiinae, within the Serranidae. Smith (1961) elevates them to full
family rank of their own, and he bases his reasons for doing so on dentition, on the absence of a supramaxilla, on possessing larger scales, and
on the constantly present lunate caudal fin. While these are rather technical
points, I find it convenient to think of them as a separate (but very closely
related) group, mainly because all the really common Anthiid species are
small to very small, varying from about 3 to at most 12 cm. This is not
at all scientific, especially as at least one genus, *Holanthias,* attains 70 cm.
But as I have yet to see *Holanthias* about the reefs, I may perhaps be
forgiven for being less than logical.

Anthiids are mostly small, brilliantly coloured fish of the reefs. They
occur in shoals and are rarely solitary; shoal size varies enormously from
a few individuals (usually in shallower water) to vast aggregates (usually

in deeper water). Most species include golds and reds in their splendid livery. They are similar in shape to the Rock Cods; but, in contrast, all possess rather large lunate or concave tails.

The distribution of the Anthiids in the Western Indian Ocean is general, although they have not been recorded from the central Seychelles. The most common species, *Anthiae squamipinnis,* apparently is Indo-Pacific in distribution.

Anthias squamipinnis 12 cm. Jewelfish.
See Colour Plate 2, No 4; brilliant golden-orange, colour not unlike that of the freshwater goldfish; a purple-edged reddish bar extends from eye to pectoral fin base. Caudal fin deeply lunate, lobes become filamentous with age. The 3rd dorsal fin spine is filamentous, and is much longer in the male fish, which is thus easily distinguished. Mostly on coral reefs, in small shoals in shallows, occasionally solitary individuals are encountered in shallow water about corals. D X 17-18; A III 7-9; L.l. 40-44; Tr 2-3/14-17; 25-26 gill-rakers; Depth 2.7-3.0.

APOGONIDAE: Cardinal fishes

The common name Cardinal conjures in the mind vivid red fishes; unfortunately this is only true of a few species. The great majority, though attractively coloured, are not red.

Cardinal fish are extremely common, often abundant, in various ecological niches in lagoonal shallows, which appear to be the preferred habitat for many species; a few are common in slightly deeper water, around inner reefs and under rocky or coral overhangs.

They are small fishes, up to 10 cm in length, of conventional shape, with two separate dorsal fins. Identification is based largely on colour and markings and is not always easy. Many of the common species have one to several dark horizontal lines running the length of the fish; some possess a conspicuous black spot on the second dorsal fin; others distinctive bars on their heads or bodies.

Most, if not all, species indulge in parental care of the eggs, and it is the male which undertakes this task. Blobs of sticky eggs, often brightly coloured, are incubated in the mouth of the male; these tend to distend the mouth and throat and males can often be distinguished in this way.

The Apogonidae are fairly voracious predators, feeding on larval fishes, crustacea and worms.

Ostorhinchus fleurieu 12 cm.
See Colour Plate 3, No 1; the two brilliant iridescent blue eyestripes, continued across the gill cover, are distinctive. Common, often abundant;

always found in rocky holes or under coral or rocky overhangs, in small shoals. Usually in deeper water (2-3 metres), but also frequently encountered in shallows. D VII+I 9; A II 8; L.l. 25-27; Tr 2/6-7; 15-17 gill-rakers; Depth 2.5.

Paramia quinquelineata 10 cm.
See Colour Plate 3, No 2; five horizontal dark lines, black edging to front of first dorsal; round yellow spot with central black dot on caudal peduncle. D VI+I 9; A II 8; L.l. 25; Tr. 2/6; gill-rakers 12-15; Depth about 3.5.

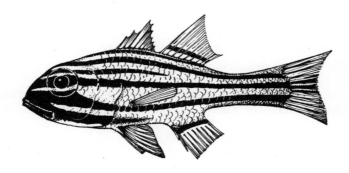

Ostorhinchus cyanosoma

Ostorhinchus cyanosoma 7 cm.
6-7 longitudinal dark stripes along body; area between stripes on head, to gill covers, brilliant iridescent pale blue, two stripes run through large eye. Occurs mainly in lagoons, in small shoals, often among sea-urchin spines. This protective habitat is sometimes shared with *Paramia quinquelineata*. D VII+I 9; A II 8; L.l. 25; Tr. 2/6; gill-rakers 15-16; Depth about 3.0.

Allied species:
Apogon nigripes 5 cm.
Not illustrated; humped back; metallic brown on dorsal surfaces, with irregular bars tapering vertically down sides; fins pink. Common in small shoals, among seagrass beds only. D VI+I 8; A II 8; L.l. 23; Tr 2/7; 20-23 gill-rakers; Depth 2.0-2.5.
Apogonichthyoides nigripinnis 7 cm.
Not illustrated; dusky grey, with broad vertical blackish bars across body from first dorsal to pectorals, second dorsal to anal fin, and across caudal peduncle. Distinguishing character a large white-

39

margined dark ocellus, on first bar, between first dorsal and pelvic fin. Common, often abundant in low-tide shallows, under rocks and in crevices; in twos and threes, more rarely in small shoals. D VII+I 9; A II 8; L.l. 23; Tr 1/6; gill-rakers 9-13; Depth about 2.4.

CARANGIDAE: Caranx, Trevallys; Kole Kole (S); Carangues (Sey)

The Carangidae cannot, strictly speaking, be described as reef fish, although they are frequently seen along reefs, in deeper water. Most species attain a good size, varying from 60 to 120 cm; they are swift, strong shoaling swimmers of the waters beyond the reef and all are carnivorous. The family is worldwide in distribution, and members are found well outside the tropics; many species are considered fine game fish, and several are good eating. Several species (especially *Caranx*) are known as Kingfish, but in Eastern Africa this refers more particularly to *Scomberomorus commerson* (Scomberomoridae). Included in the Carangidae are the very attractive Rainbow Runners, *Elagatis bipinnulatus,* and possibly the Canadian Runner or Cobia, *Rachycentron canadus,* although Smith (1965) gives the latter fish family rank. Most species of *Caranx,* a genus of economic importance, are known indiscriminately as Kole Kole in Eastern Africa.

The body is more or less compressed, robust; caudal peduncle very slender, tail always forked. The teeth are small, often absent. The slender peduncle and deeply forked tail are characteristic of the family.

The juveniles of one species in the family are frequently encountered in the lagoon. This is *Gnathanodon speciosus,* which is an attractive fish when young, and which has a characteristic and charming habit. These fish, often two or more, will accompany a fishwatcher for hundreds of metres across a lagoon, swimming close alongside, or underneath, the swimmer. They will follow a human into the shallows, where the water depth is no more than 10 cm. When sub-adult, they aggregate into shoals (see Colour Plate 3, No 3). This behaviour is consistent throughout the family.

Another member shows an interesting similarity in behaviour: the Pilot fish (*Naucrates ductor*) associates in much the same way with sharks.

Gnathanodon speciosus Adults to 120 cm. Carangue Chasseur (Sey), Golden Trevally (Q).
Juveniles as illustrated in Colour Plate 3, No 3; smaller fish (5-10 cm) brilliant golden-yellow or yellow, with black cross bars, which fade with age. Adults rarely seen in shallow water. D I+VIII+I 18-21; A II+I 15-17; 20 gill-rakers; Depth about 2.5.

MULLIDAE: Red Mullets, Surmullets, Goatfishes; Mkundaji (S); Capucin Rouget (Sey)

While reds are the dominant colours in most species of Red Mullets, the two common species dealt with, *Pseudupeneus macronema* and *Upeneus tragula,* are normally sand-coloured or faintly pink, with various black markings. The former species is often seen to blush deep pinky red; I am not sure whether this is an emotional response but it can obviously be controlled at will. One of their other common names, Goatfishes, is perhaps a better descriptive name, as all species possess one pair of simple long sensitive barbels on the chin. The barbels are the 'goatees' of the fish, named after the style of beard once popular. These can be retracted to lie flush with the chin and may not be immediately noticeable, but if the fish are watched quietly, the barbels will be lowered. They feel their way over sand with their barbels, which are sensitive organs of feeling and taste used to locate their food, presumably crustaceans and worms, which are then extracted and ingested.

These feeding habits indicate that Goatfish are most likely to be found in or near sandy areas of the lagoon and inner reefs, and this is so, where they occur in small shoals of half a dozen or more fish.

The body is fairly elongate, of characteristic shape, with a large head, and two separate dorsal fins; the tail is forked.

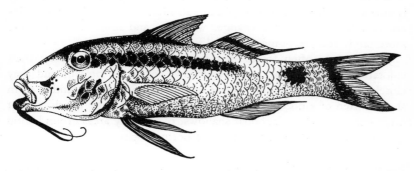

Pseudupeneus macronema

Pseudupeneus macronema 30 cm.
Sandy-coloured to pinkish red; one broad black horizontal stripe from front of eye along upper part of side, ending under the second dorsal fin; black spot at caudal peduncle; barbels large (*macro*=large; *nema*=thread or barbel). A light-coloured saddle-like spot is sometimes visible on back behind second dorsal. Tail not barred or marked. D VIII+I 8; A I 6; L.l. 28-30; Tr 3/7; 24 gill-rakers; Depth 3.5.

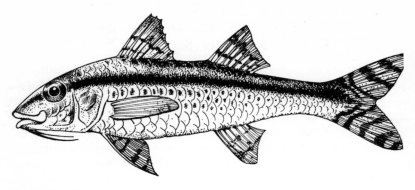

Upeneus tragula

Upeneus tragula 25 cm. Mottled Goatfish (Q).
Sandy coloured or brownish, head and body mottled with black spots; dark horizontal stripe from eye to tail base; tail with oblique dark cross-bars. D VII-VIII+I 7-8; A I 6-7; L.l. 30-32; Tr 2/6; 16-18 gill-rakers; Depth about 4.3.

PLATACIDAE: Batfish, Tuguu (S) Poule D'Eau (Sey)

The single common species, *Platax pinnatus,* is unmistakable; the body is almost circular, and in young and sub-adults the dorsal and anal fins are very large. The shape changes with age, and adult fish, which are more rarely seen, have more normal fins.

Juveniles are often found in tidal shore-line and reef pools; their coloration is cryptic, being sandy-yellow, yellow or brown, and they closely resemble a dead leaf or piece of seaweed. Sub-adults tend to form shoals, often of a dozen fish or more, and it is this stage which is most often encountered, in lagoonal shallows, over sandy areas around coral gardens, or near jetties, fish traps or mooring ropes.

Platax pinnatus 60 cm, more frequently seen as sub-adults at 15-30 cm.
Easily recognised, see Colour Plate 3, No 4; brownish, with two vertical blackish bars. D V 28-38 (spines almost concealed); A III 24-29; 8-10 gill-rakers; Depth 1.0 (body as deep as long).

POMACANTHIDAE: Angelfish, Brinzi (S)

The Pomacanthidae are one of three families of fish that are archetypical of coral reefs: the other two, dealt with in subsequent sections, are the Butterfly fish and the Damselfish. Angelfish are among the most attractive of all reef inhabiting species, both by virtue of their graceful shape and outline, and their brilliant colours.

In most species the adult body is laterally compressed and vaguely rectangular in outline, with rounded soft dorsal and anal fins. Their most distinctive field character is the strong, prominent spine at the angle of the pre-opercle. The teeth are fine and bristle-like, being used to scrape coral polyps, algae and crustacea off coral and rocks.

In at least three species, juvenile coloration and patterns are remarkably and completely different from those of the adult fish. The successive changes in two of the more common species are illustrated below; illustrations of juveniles and adults of *Pomacanthodes imperator* and *Pomacanthops semicirculatus* are given in Colour Plate 4.

Juveniles are most frequently seen in lagoon shallows and in quieter, shallower water around inner reefs and coral gardens. They seem at this stage to be at least partially territorial in behaviour, in that the same juvenile can be found occupying the same rocky or coral cleft or hole, or deep overhang, over a period of many days. Juvenile coloration is similar in several species, being black, with white and iridescent blue lines variously arranged. Adults free-swimming, always around and near living reefs.

While Angelfish cannot be described as abundant anywhere, they may sometimes be locally common and the juveniles and adults of at least one of the species are usually to be seen during an hour's quiet fish-watching.

Pomacanthodes imperator showing pattern development from juvenile to adult.

Pomacanthodes imperator 45 cm. Emperor Angelfish, Brinzi (S).
Juveniles and adults as illustrated in Colour Plate 4, Nos 1 and 2; changes
with growth as above. D XIV 19-22; A III 18-21; Depth 1.5-1.8.

Pomacanthops semicirculatus showing pattern development from juvenile to adult.

Pomacanthops semicirculatus 45 cm. Koran Angelfish, Brinzi (S).
Juveniles and adults as illustrated in Colour Plate 4, Nos 3 and 4; changes
with growth as above. D XII 21-23; A III 20-22; Depth about 1.7.

Pomacanthodes chrysurus 30 cm.
Adults as illustrated in Colour Plate 5, No 1; juvenile essentially similar
to adult, small specimens (10-15 cm) wear adult livery.

Allied species:
  Pomacanthops filamentosus 30 cm.
  Not illustrated; purplish-blue, with golden-yellow blotch on side.

With age, soft dorsal fin elongates and may become filamentous if not damaged.

Centropyge multispinis 15 cm.

Not illustrated; an atypical species: adult behaviour and habitat preference as for juveniles of *Pomacanthops* and *Pomacanthodes*: always encountered in shallows, under coral rocks and in holes among coral debris. Very wary. Small, dark-coloured, blackish; oblique cross-bars on body discernible in good light only; brilliant blue edging to pelvic fins.

CHAETODONTIDAE: Butterfly fishes, Kitatange (S), Papillons (Sey)

The Chaetodontidae or Butterfly fishes are among the most gracefully agile and attractive of reef fish. All species have deep, laterally compressed bodies and the majority a small, pointed snout. The teeth are bristle-like in many species, an attribute used in naming one genus, and the family (*chaeta,* a bristle; *-don,* tooth).

Both dorsal and anal fins are well-developed and gracefully curved, and add much to the attractive symmetry of the fish.

The pointed protruding snout is an adaptation to the feeding habits of the family. Species with bristle-like teeth rip off individual coral polyps or small anemones; those with flattened chisel-like teeth crop coral and polyps together.

Butterfly fish do not grow to a large size; few attain 30 cm (*Chaetodon lineolatus* may, and is probably the largest species) and adult specimens vary between 15 and 25 cm.

Most species conform to a characteristic shape and are distinguished mainly by markings. All have a vertical eyestripe, almost invariably black. A few species exhibit marked differences between juvenile and adult forms. *Chaetodon lunula* juveniles are the most likely to be encountered and a young fish of this species is illustrated below.

The fifteen species of *Chaetodon* described in the text and illustrated may be divided into those having a body colour yellow, orange or brown (six species) and those with a white, greyish or silvery-grey body, disregarding fin colour, which is generally orange or yellowish (nine species). Colour Plate 5, No 2 illustrates one species in each colour group. One further species, *C. meyeri,* has a spectacular blue body (the only Butterfly fish in our area so coloured) with uniquely arranged black lines, and cannot be mistaken for any other.

The following characters help to determine the species underwater:
i) presence of narrow, often black, lines, and their arrangement (vertical, horizontal, diagonal, V-shaped) on the sides of the body;

ii) presence of broad black bars (as opposed to lines);

iii) presence of small definite spots on the body (two species only, *kleini* and *gutatissimus*); presence of large black ocellar spot on body (three species only, all yellow: *unimaculatus, zanzibarensis, bennetti*).

With the Butterfly fishes I have described most species that are likely to be encountered and have not confined descriptions to the common ones only. I have indicated whether they are apparently abundant, common or rare; these classes obviously will not be correct for all localities in the Western Indian Ocean. Species described as rare or uncommon may be locally or seasonally common, or even abundant.

Chaetodon auriga 15 cm. Papillon Jaune (Sey), Thread-fin Butterfly fish (Q). See Colour Plate 5, No 2. Body white, with two groups of diagonal bluish-black lines set at right angles; soft dorsal and anal fins orange. Black spot on soft dorsal; 5th, 6th or 7th ray of soft dorsal filamentous. Common. D XII-XIII 23-26; A III 20-21; L.l. about 30; 13-14 gillrakers; Depth about 1.5.

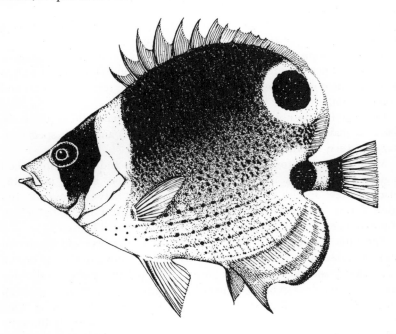

Chaetodon lunula (juvenile)

C. lunula 20 cm.
See Colour Plate 5, No 2. Body rich orange brown with diagonal reddish

stripes; reddish spots on breast. Pure white area behind eyestripe, then two large curved black marks as indicated in colour illustration. Black stripe along back below dorsal fin, ending in a blob at base of tail. Juveniles, as above, are without this stripe: instead, there is a black ocellus with a pale orange halo on soft dorsal. Unmistakable, common, often locally abundant. Juveniles in reef and rocky shore pools. D XII 23-25; A III 18-20; L.l. about 38; 13 gill-rakers; Depth about 1.5.

C. trifasciatus 13 cm. Papillon (Sey).
See Colour Plate 5, No 3. Characteristic shape; snout rounded, not pointed as in other Chaetodons. Body rich orange yellow, with horizontal brownish-red lines. Black bar below soft dorsal and anal fins. Three black bars on head: at extremity of face, the eyestripe, and a third behind eye. A gloriously attractive species, mostly in pairs; common. D XII-XIII 21-23; A III 19-20; L.l. about 38; 13 gill-rakers; Depth about 1.5.

C. melanotus 13 cm.
See Colour Plate 5, No 4. Body whitish with black diagonal lines and dots; darkish area beneath dorsal fin. Widespread, but not common. D XII 19-20; A III 17-18; L.l. about 35; 9 gill-rakers; Depth about 1.7.

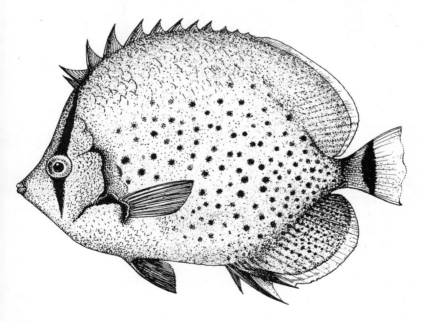

Chaetodon guttatissimus

C. guttatissimus 10 cm.

Pale coloured; whitish or occasionally with very pale yellowish hue; numerous small black spots on body. Distinctive eye stripe, pale centre, black border. Unmistakable, fairly common. *C. kleini,* 15 cm, is the only other spotted *Chaetodon*. It differs from *guttatissimus* in having a dull orange body, with numerous distinctive white spots. Snout black, rear of dorsal and anal fins darkish. Locally common. D XIII 20-23; A III 17-20; L.l. about 40; 12 gill-rakers; Depth about 1.7.

Chaetodon vagabundus

C. vagabundus 23 cm. Criss-cross Butterfly fish (Q).

Body whitish to silvery grey with two groups of diagonal lines set at right angles; soft dorsal and anal fins orange. Curved black bar from soft dorsal to anal fin. Common, often encountered in the lagoon, far from coral. D XII-XIII 23-26; A III 20-22; L.l. about 35; 11 gill-rakers; Depth about 1.5.

C. lineolatus 30 cm. Papillon Jaeune (Sey); Lined Butterfly fish (Q).

Body silvery grey with numerous vertical black lines; black bar below soft dorsal; broad black eyestripe. Probably the largest species. Common. D XII 24-28; A III 20-21; L.l. about 23; 12 gill-rakers; Depth about 1.5.

48

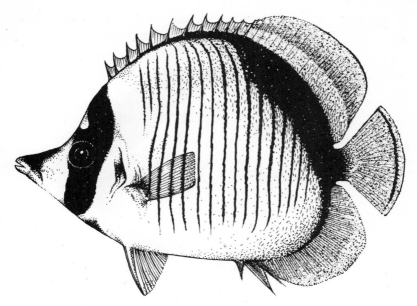

Chaetodon lineolatus

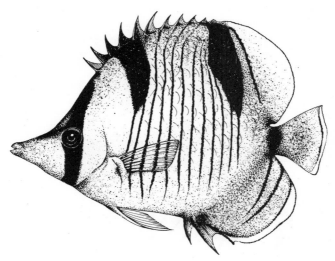

Chaetodon falcula

C. falcula 20 cm.
Body whitish with vertical lines; two triangular black bars on back, one at front and one at rear of spiny dorsal. Widespread, but not common.

D XII-XIII 24-28; A III 19-23; L.l. about 25; 12 gill-rakers; Depth about 1.5.

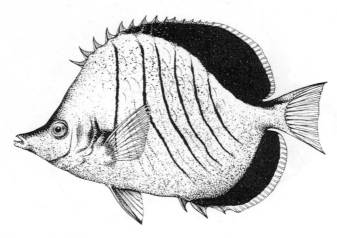

Chaetodon xanthocephalus

C. xanthocephalus 18 cm.
Body bluish-grey to silvery with six slightly curved vertical lines; dorsal and anal fins orange. Head, snout and breast orange in juvenile; lower part of head and breast orange in adult. Eyestripe narrow, not extensive. This fish has a distinctive steep curve to its back along the soft dorsal (see illustration). Widespread, but not common. D XIII-XIV 25-27; A III 23-24; L.l. about 40; Depth 1.5.

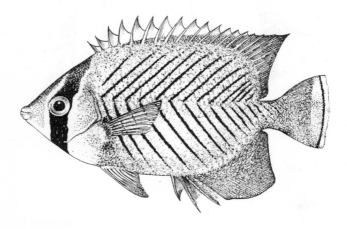

Chaetodon trifascialis

C. trifascialis 13 cm. Right-angled Butterfly fish (Q).
Body silvery grey to white with numerous V-shaped lines, directed forwards; soft dorsal ends in a distinctive point; eyestripe broad. Common. D XIV 15-17; A IV-V 15-16; L.l. about 25; Tr 8/12; about 25 gill-rakers; Depth about 1.8.

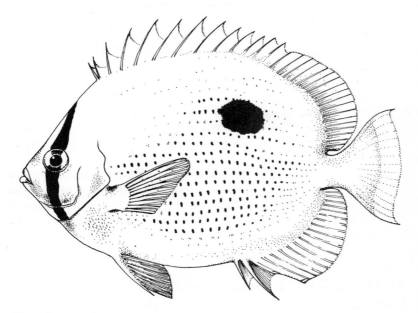

Chaetodon zanzibarensis

C. zanzibarensis 20 cm.
Body yellow; large black ocellus on back, below soft dorsal. *C. unimaculatus* (20 cm) is similar, but may be distinguished by black edging to rear of dorsal and anal fins, and black bar at base of tail. *C. bennetti* is also similar, but ocellus has a blue halo, and there are two blue stripes arranged as an inverted oblique V, from behind eye to anal fin. Eyestripe edged blue. None of these species may be described as common.
C. bennetti: D XIV 17-18; A III 15-16; gill-rakers 13-14; Depth 1.5.
C. unimaculatus: D XIII 22-23; A III 19-20; gill-rakers 12; Depth 1.5.

Heniochus acuminatus 20 cm. Coachman.
See Colour Plate 6, No 1. Body whitish, with two broad diagonal cross bars; great elongation of 4th dorsal spine to form a pennant. Unmistakable, but often confused with the Moorish Idol, *Zanclus canescens,* where body bars are vertical, not diagonal (see Colour Plate 6, No 2). Common,

often abundant in shoals. D XI-XII 23-28; A III 15-19; L.l. about 45; 11 gill-rakers; Depth about 1.3.

Allied species:

Chaetodon leucopleura 15 cm.
Not illustrated. Body whitish; few horizontal red lines on belly and red spots on breast. Fins yellow. Widespread but not common.

Forcipiger longirostris 15 cm.
Not illustrated. Snout very elongated, tubular; body bright yellow without vertical bars; upper half of head black, lower half of face, breast and snout white. Small black ocellus on fin below tail. Uncommon.

Chelmon rostratus 15 cm.
Not illustrated. Snout elongated, tubular; body silvery, with four reddish brown vertical bars lined blue; black ocellar spot with pale blue halo. Rare.

Forcipiger and *Chelmon* are known as the Long-snouted or Long-nosed Butterfly fish. The extraordinarily long snouts of these two species are distinctive and may indicate that they exploit minute crevices in coral for food (such as worms and crustacea), a food area denied the less well-endowed Butterfly fish.

ACANTHURIDAE: Surgeon fishes and Unicorn fishes; Kangaja and Puju (S), Chirurgien and Licorne (Sey)

Body shape characteristic, with a movable spine or scalpel (Surgeons) or one or two bony plates with fixed sharp keels (Unicorns) on each side at base of tail. This feature is diagnostic, the scalpels giving the family its popular name. Some, but not all, species of Unicorns develop a single forward-projecting horn, or distinct bump, on the forehead. Gregarious (except possibly the Sailfin Surgeons), usually in twos and threes, often in large shoals.

The Acanthuridae are herbivores. They are almost all grazers, cropping close-growing algal mats off rocks; some (*Naso*) feed on upright forms of seaweed (*Sargassum*); one genus (*Ctenochaetus*) feeds on plant detritus; and there is a record of at least one species which feeds, atypically, on coral polyps. They have a very long thin-walled gut or intestine, an attribute of most herbivorous animals.

The young of all Acanthurids are almost circular and transparent with a silvery abdomen. They are so different from the adults that they were first described as different fishes, and given the name *Acronurus*. The name is now applied to the post-larval stages.

The razor-sharp spines of the Surgeon fishes, housed in a groove or sheath on either side of the base of the tail, are movable, but they are not erectile; they cannot be erected or flicked out at will. They are attached or hinged to the backbone by a strong ligament which is independent of the powerful musculature of the tail. When the fish curves its body, the tip of the spine on the convex side is bared; if this is snagged on anything the spine is unsheathed and the blade is thus enabled to cut.

Aggressive behaviour consists of fully erecting the dorsal and anal fins and flexing the body convexly towards the object against which aggression is directed. The tail is often vibrated rapidly from side to side, thus repeatedly exposing the tip of the spine.

The sharp often forward-projecting fixed keels of the Unicorn fishes and the spines of the Surgeons are not considered toxic, although this has been the subject of some controversy. In any event, they are capable of inflicting deep wounds and it is advisable to handle these fishes with care.

With a few notable exceptions, the Acanthurids are perhaps the most difficult to identify of all reef fish. Few species are brilliantly coloured, the body colour mostly being brown. Many are able to vary their colour from beige, through light and dark browns, often almost to black. During these rapid shifts in colour, the more helpful field marks, such as black spots or bars, become less obvious. Apart from the Unicorns, and the Sailfin Surgeons which have enormously exaggerated or elevated dorsal and anal fins, the body shape does not vary greatly and is of little help in identification. They often consort in parties of mixed species. (See Colour Plate 6, No 3.)

In common with herbivorous animals in general, they are wary and, unless engrossed in feeding, are difficult subjects for the photographer.

The Surgeons are also known as Lancet fishes, or Tangs.

Acanthurus leucosternon 23 cm. White-breasted Surgeon, Blue Tang.
See Colour Plate 6, No 3; unmistakable; body colour pale to bright blue, white breast, black face. Dorsal fin bright yellow, edged blue; anal and pelvic fins white. Common in most localities, especially in deep lagoons and deeper reef pools, frequently in small, but apparently never in dense, shoals. D IX 28-30; A III 25-27; 12 short gill-rakers; Depth 1.8.

A. triostegus 23 cm. Convict Surgeon.
See Colour Plate 6, No 3; body colour white to whitish grey, with four more or less evenly-spaced vertical black bars; two black spots on caudal peduncle. Very common in reef pools, particularly juveniles and younger specimens. Adults often in small, loose shoals. D IX-X 21-25; A III 19-22; 16 short divided gill-rakers; Depth 1.8.

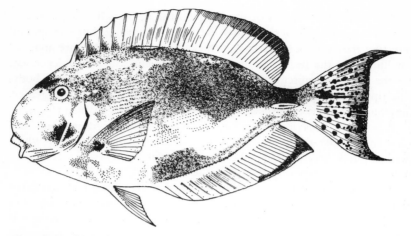

Acanthurus dussumieri

A. dussumieri 45 cm. (Synonym=*A. bariene*).
The only commonly occurring Surgeon with dark blue spots on caudal fin, an unmistakable identity mark. Remarkable colour changes; body beige to brown with longitudinal blue lines, orange bar through eye. Caudal fin lunate. Fairly common to common. D IX 24-26; A III 23-25; 13 feeble gill-rakers; Depth about 2.0.

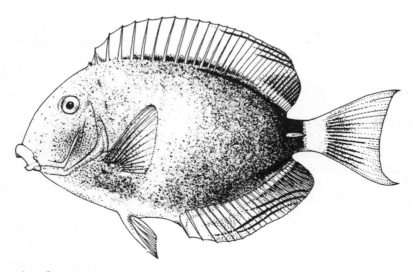

Acanthurus mata

A. mata 30 cm. (Synonym=*A. lineolatus*).
Body colour variable, usually very dark, brown; best field characteristics
are white base to caudal fin and white spine sheath. Fairly common to
common, occasionally in large shoals. D IX 24-25; A III 23-24; 15 feeble
gill-rakers; Depth about 2.0.

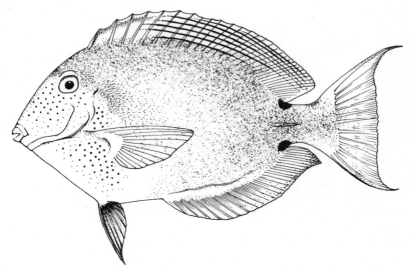

Acanthurus nigroris

A. nigroris 23 cm.
Body colour variable, usually very dark brown; best field characteristics
of last rays of dorsal and anal fins, the critical identification mark. Small
blue spots on head. Fairly common to common, often in deeper reef
pools.

A. nigrofuscus 15 cm.
Not illustrated; very similar to *A. nigroris* and may be confused with
this species. The black spot at the base of the dorsal fin is, however,
comparatively large, the caudal more lunate, and the head and chest
have russet or brown (not blue) spots. Juveniles bright yellow, with blue
markings on head.

A. tennenti 30 cm.
Velvety brown with two easily observed black 'commas' behind gill
cover above pectoral fin; orange patch before eye. D IX 23; A III 23;
16 gill-rakers; Depth about 2.1.

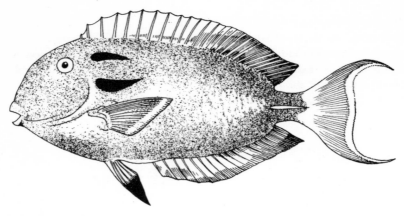

Acanthurus tennenti

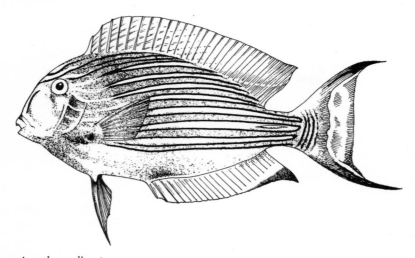

Acanthurus lineatus

A. lineatus 30 cm. Lined Surgeon.
Body colour bright orange, with horizontal bright blue lines bordered with dark blue; face similarly lined. Belly bluish. Colours iridescent. In shoals in deeper waters of lagoon or in deep reef pools. Common, easily recognised; the only Surgeon with horizontal lines. D IX 26-27; A III 25-27; 11 short gill-rakers; Depth about 2.0.

Zebrasoma veliferum 30 cm. Sailfin Surgeon fish.
Dark brown; sides of face and chin with yellowish spots; broad lightish (often yellowish or white) vertical bands on sides, often broken bands

on fins. Relatively enormous dorsal and anal fins, diagnostic of the genus, render recognition easy. The closely related *Zebrasoma flavescens* (20 cm), the Yellow Sailfin Surgeon fish, is more or less identical in shape to *veliferum,* but is bright chrome yellow in colour. Solitary, or in twos and threes; never in shoals.

For *veliferum*, D IV 28-33; A III 22-26; P15-17; gill rakers 9-10; Depth 1.8-2.0.

For *flavescens,* D V 23-26; A III 19-22; P14-16; gill-rakers 11-12; Depth 1.4-1.8.

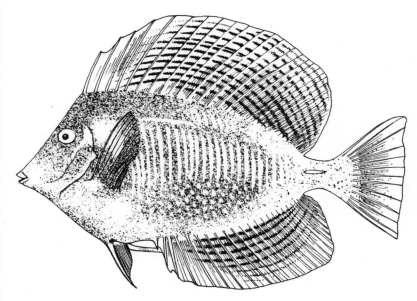

Zebrasoma veliferum

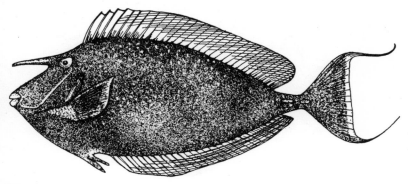

Naso unicornis

Naso unicornis 60 cm. Unicorn, Puju (S) Corne (Sey), Brown Unicorn fish (Q).
Easily recognised, outline on p 57; colour variable, brown to greyish; dorsal and anal fins light orange, with dark blue edges; two keels, with bluish halos; lips light blue; horn lengthens with age, longer in males. D V-VI 27-30; A II 26-29; nine short gill-rakers; Depth 2-2.5.

Callicanthus litturatus 60 cm. Unicorn, Licorne (Sey).
See Colour Plate 6, No 4; body brown; dorsal fin, area around eye and chest and keels bright orange; long caudal fin streamers and keels good recognition characteristics. Solitary or in pairs, about coral reefs in deeper water. D VI 28-31; A II 28-32; nine short gill-rakers; Depth 2.5-3.0.

MONODACTYLIDAE: Moonfish; Lalua (S); Breton (Sey); Diamondfish (Q)

The single common species of Moonfish is easily recognisable by the deep silver, laterally compressed diamond-shaped body, and the very symmetrical dorsal and anal fins. This extremely widespread species enters creeks, estuaries and fresh water. It always occurs in shoals, often large, moves nervously and rapidly through the water, and is easily startled into swift flight.

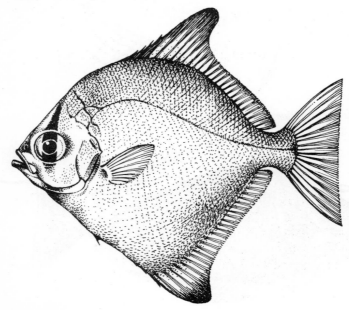

Monodactylus argenteus

Monodactylus argenteus 20 cm. Rambale or Vipepeo (S).
Outline as illustrated above; diamond shaped silvery or silvery-grey body; fins yellow; dorsal and anal fins symmetrical, rounded tips of these fins black; eyestripe present. The young have two crossbars, which fade with age. In shoals, about large coral bosses or rocks. D VII-VIII 28-30; A III 28-32; V I 2-4; L.l. 50-60; 16-19 gill-rakers; Depth 1.3-1.5.

ZANCLIDAE: Moorish Idol; Kitatange (S); Tranchoir (Sey)

Unmistakable, easily recognised, the 3rd-7th dorsal spines are long and pennant-like. In small shoals about coral; widespread and common throughout the Western Indian Ocean, extending eastwards to the Pacific. It is said that Muslim fishermen respect these fishes. Smith (1965) has described Moorish Idols as rather pompous fish, and this description cannot be bettered.

Zanclus canescens (=Zanclus cornutus) 23 cm.
See Colour Plate 6, No 2; mouth prominent, pointed; 3rd-7th dorsal spines elongated to form a pennant. This species is often confused with the Coachman, *Heniochus acuminatus* (Colour Plate 6, No 1), which also carries a pennant and similar livery. In *Zanclus* the two cross-bars on the body are vertical; in *Heniochus* they are oblique. D VII 38-41; A III 32-35; Depth 1.0 (body about as deep as long).

GERRIDAE: Silver-bellies; Chaa (S); Breton (Sey)

The Silver-bellies are often the first fish to be noticed when goggling from sandy or flat, rocky shoreline shallows in lagoons or sheltered bays. They are common, often abundant small silvery or grey fishes which occasionally occur in great shoals.

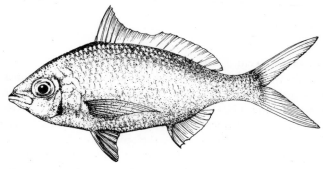

Gerres oyena

Gerres oyena 25 cm.

Outline diagram p 59; darkish above, silvery below; a few irregular narrow dark areas from back down sides; black marks at front of dorsal fin; tail forked. Mouth protrusible downwards, frequently seen nosing about in sand. Shallow sandy flats in lagoons and creeks; mostly in small shoals, often abundant. D IX 10-11; A III 7; L.l. 35-38; Tr 5/11; seven gill-rakers; Depth 2.3-2.8.

KYPHOSIDAE: Rudderfishes; Kukusi (S); Poisson D'Ail (Sey); Drummer (Q)

Rudderfishes have oval bodies, a smallish head and a large strong tail, with a suitably robust caudal peduncle. The teeth are set in a small mouth. Rather elegant looking fishes of deeper water (3-5 metres), they are encountered near coral gardens in deeper lagoons and often around solitary large rocks. They apparently feed mainly on algae and small crustacea.

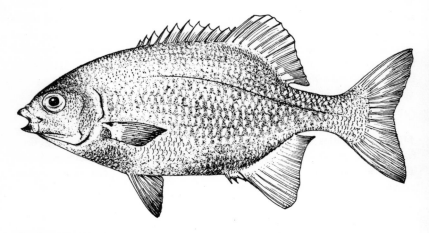

Kyphosus vaigiensis

Kyphosus vaigiensis 60 cm. Kusi or Kufi (S).

Outline as illustrated above; grey-blue, with narrow bronzy lines along head and length of body. The soft dorsal fin is lower than the spiny dorsal in outline and lobes of the tail are pointed; these characters help to distinguish *vaigiensis* from the very similar, closely related *K. cinerascens,* where the soft dorsal is higher than the spiny dorsal, the anal fin proportionately large, so also the rounded tail lobes. D XI 13-15; A III 13-14; L.l. about 55; Tr about 11/16; 21-24 gill-rakers; Depth about 2.3.

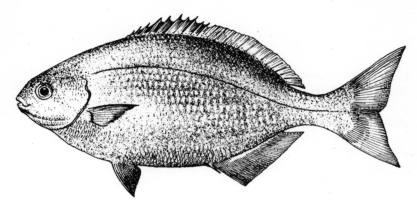

Kyphosus cinerascens

K. cinerascens 30 cm.
Outline as illustrated above; silvery-grey, with bronzy lines along sides.
Soft dorsal and anal fins large in comparison with *vaigiensis*. D XI 12;
A III 11-12; L.l. about 60; Tr 10/18; 18-20 gill-rakers; Depth about 2.3.

PEMPHERIDAE: Sweepers

The most characteristic feature of the common Sweeper, *Pempheris oualensis,* is the body shape: the stomach is deep and slopes obliquely to a relatively small caudal peduncle, rendering the fish faintly reminiscent of Mr Pickwick. Sweepers are encountered in lagoons and tidal reef pools; the young fishes (2-5 cm) form vast shoals of hundreds. They have a typical manner of swimming, seeming to move along in rather jerky movements, following the beats of the pectoral fins.

Pempheris oualensis 20 cm.
Shape unmistakable, see Colour Plate 7, No 1; colour reddish brown to coppery pink. Juveniles in large shoals in tidal pools, or around isolated coral or rock bosses; adults always near protective cover. Judging by the ratio of small fry (2-5 cm) to adult fish (15-20 cm), it seems the slow-swimming defenceless Sweepers are a significant source of food to the carnivores of the lagoon and reef. D VI 9-10; A III 39-45; L.l. 55-65; Tr 4/15; 20-21 gill-rakers; Depth 2.3-2.5.

PENTAPODIDAE

Related to the Snappers (Lutjanidae), the more or less common species of the Pentapodidae are not particularly remarkable fish, neither in form nor habits. As there is, however, a good chance of encountering one or both, they are described briefly. The eyes are noticeably large.

Gnathodentex aureolineatus 30 cm. Carandine (Sey).
See Colour Plate 7, No 2; solitary or in small aggregates, often about coral debris or rocky rubble, or near inner reefs. D X 10; A III 8-9; L.l. about 75; Tr 6/20; six gill-rakers; Depth about 2.8.

Allied species:
  Monotaxis grandoculis 60 cm.
  Not illustrated. Grey; huge heavy head with very large eyes (hence the name). Near coral and rocks in deeper lagoons. D X 10; A III 9; L.l. 45; Tr 6/14; five gill-rakers; Depth 2.5.

LUTJANIDAE: Snappers; Kukusi (S); Sea Perch (Q)

The common Snappers are mostly brilliantly coloured fishes of the lagoon and reef; they are social and have a tendency to shoal. These are often vast, and a shoal of a hundred or more *Lutjanus kasmira,* the Blue-lined Snapper, is one of the more breathtaking sights of the reef. The body is robust, the dorsal continuous; the mouth is large and contains well-developed canine-like teeth. When removed from the water, the jaws tend to snap shut with convulsive force. The species are readily distinguished by colour and markings.

Lutjanus kasmira 30 cm. Blue-lined Snapper; Tembo, Mbawaa (S); Madras (Sey); Blue-banded Sea Perch (Q).
Brilliantly coloured, see Colour Plate 7, No 3; body yellow, four longitudinal bright blue lines from head to tail; head brownish or bluish above. Mainly in shoals, often vast, about reefs; smaller fish in quieter waters of lagoons, in twos and threes or more. D X 13-16; A III 8; L.l. about 50; Tr 10/17; 15 gill-rakers, some rudimentary; Depth about 2.8.

Lutjanus johni 38 cm. Tembo (S), Ziebelo (Sey).
See Colour Plate 7, No 4; large oval dark patch on flank over lateral line; scales above lateral line run **parallel** with lateral line; caudal, soft dorsal and anal fins yellow, few (4-5) narrow yellow lines along silvery-yellow sides, dorsal part of fish olive-green to brownish. Younger fish common, sometimes abundant. Adults about reef in small shoals. D X 13-14; A III 8-9; L.l. 45-48; Tr 6/12; 12-13 gill-rakers, some rudimentary; Depth 2.6.

This fish may be confused with *Lutjanus fulviflamma,* which is also yellowish, and also has the large oval dark patch on the flank. In *fulviflamma* the scales above the lateral line run **obliquely** to, not parallel with, the line. This distinguishing characteristic is surprisingly easily observed under water. Details are as follows.

Lutjanus fulviflamma 30 cm. Carpe (Sey), Black-spot Sea-Perch (Q). Large dark oval patch on flank over lateral line; scales above lateral line **oblique**; fins yellow; several narrow orange or yellow lines along sides. General appearance is often more yellow than *Lutjanus johni,* but this is not a good underwater characteristic, as *fulviflamma* is a variable species. D X 13-14; A III 8-9; L.l. 45-50; Tr 7/14; 7-9 obvious gill-rakers; Depth about 2.8.

Lutjanus sebae

Lutjanus sebae Numba (S), Bourgeois (Sey) Red Emperor (Q).
Attains 60 cm when fully adult, but usually only young and sub-adults encountered around reefs and in lagoon. Young fish pale pink, adults whitish, all stages with three vivid red transverse bands, one obliquely through eye, one vertically across body, and the third runs obliquely, in a curve, from dorsal fin across caudal peduncle to lower part of caudal fin. Unmistakable, attractive, juveniles associate with large sea urchins, where they find protection among the spines. Adults locally common in some areas; rare in others. D XI-XII 15-16; A III 9-11; L.l. 45-50; Tr 10/20; 12 gill-rakers; Depth about 2.3.

Allied species:

Lutjanus bohar 38 cm. Vara-Vara (Sey).

Not illustrated; grey, two conspicuous white spots on side, below dorsal. Young fish usually solitary, about reefs.

CAESIODIDAE: Caesios; Fusiliers; Rainbow flashers; Viunda (S)

Mostly small, brilliantly coloured fish with somewhat elongate bodies, with a single dorsal. They occur in shoals, sometimes vast, around reefs, where they present one of the more spectacular underwater scenes. Species differentiated by colour and markings; body shape constant, caudal in common species always forked.

Caesio xanthonotus 20 cm.

See Colour Plate 8, No 1; upper third, or more, yellow, middle third blue. Frequently in vast shoals about reefs.

Allied species:

Caesio caerulaureus 20 cm.

Not illustrated. Shape as for *xanthonotus*; upper half blue, not yellow; lower half pinkish; distinctive yellow horizontal line along body more or less bisecting blue upper half; dark bars along outer halves of forked caudal. Frequently in vast shoals about reefs. D X 14-15; A III 11-13; L.l. about 65; Tr. 7/15; 25 gill-rakers; Depth 3.5.

GATERINIDAE: Gaterins; Sweetlips; Fute (S)

The Gaterins are among the few reef-haunting fish that attain a modest size, several species attaining 60 cm, and are colourful. The body shape is conventional, but distinctive; robust but moderately compressed. The lips are well developed, becoming very large and prominent, often yellowish, with age. The dorsal fin is continuous.

In some papers the genus name *Plectorhynchus* is used in place of *Gaterin,* and the family referred to as the Plectorhynchidae. Smith (1962) has shown that *Gaterin* has prior claim over *Plectorhynchus,* as the former was used first by Forskal in 1775, and the latter only in 1802 by Lacepede. This is a good example of the confusion which has arisen in the naming of fish. I see no valid reason for not accepting Smith's arguments, and I use the family and specific names as used in Smith and Smith (1969).

Gaterins show changes in colours and markings with growth, but the common species are identifiable, in adult livery, at early stages. Many species are attractively colourful, and most of them are excellent eating. Economically important as food, significantly most species have Swahili names.

Gaterin flavomaculatus 60 cm. Fute (S).
See Colour Plate 8, No 2; bluish grey, with bright orange spots and short lines on body. The markings are variable with age; juveniles have continuous orange or golden lines along the body, which first change to form broken lines and then separate spots. The broken lines are retained on the head. Common about reefs, especially where seagrass meadows occur adjacent to corals. D XIII (20) 21-22; A III 7; P2, 15; L.l. about 60 tubules; Tr about 12/16; (17) 18-19 gill-rakers; Depth 2.7-2.8.

G. gaterinus 50 cm. Mlea, Nyeya (S).
See Colour Plate 8, No 3; greyish, body covered in black spots; these are larger on yellowish dorsal and anal fins. Juveniles with longitudinal stripes. Inside of mouth red. Common about reefs, often in small shoals. D XII-XIII 19-20; A III 7-8; L.l. about 70; 17-18 gill-rakers; Depth 2.5.

Allied species:
   G. orientalis 60 cm.
   Not illustrated; silvery-grey, with several (about nine) broadish longitudinal dark stripes along the length of body; yellowish caudal fin spotted and barred. Juveniles irregularly blotched, with black pectoral (pectoral fin is unmarked in adult); blotches often with orange margins. About reefs. D XIII (17-) 18; A III 7(8); P2, 16; L.l. about 65 tubules; Tr 16/22; 21-22 gill-rakers; Depth 2.6-2.8.
   G. niger 60 cm. Kimwanchi Koko (S).
   Not illustrated. Unmarked dull greyish-silver, caudal fin sometimes with pinkish tinge. Lips become very large and yellow with age. About reefs and rocky debris. D XIV 15-26; A III 7; P2, 15; L.l. 50-55 tubules; Tr 10/14; 18-19 gill-rakers; Depth 2.8.
   G. playfairi 50 cm. Mshoto (S).
   Not illustrated; dark grey, almost black in some fish, with three prominent white crossbars across back, and a fourth, less marked, across nape. Lips pinkish, large. About reefs and rocky debris. D XII 19-20; A III 7; P2, 14; L.l. about 58-60 tubules; Tr 13/25; 20-22 gill-rakers; Depth 2.4.

LETHRINIDAE: Barefaces; Kawa (S); Emperors (Q)

While the Barefaces live about coral reefs, only one species is seen commonly enough to warrant inclusion here: most members are confined to deeper reefs. They are economically important as food fish.

The common name is derived from the lack of scales on the cheek and most of the head. The body is robust, the head and mouth large and more or less pointed, with prominent lips. Most species are brightly coloured; the body shows little or no differential features, and identification is based largely on coloration. As this fades rapidly with death, considerable confusion has arisen from early descriptions of preserved specimens. The single species dealt with here is one of the duller Lethrinids.

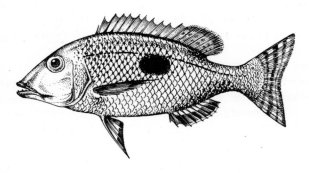

Lethrinus harak

Lethrinus harak 45 cm. Kawa, Mchakufa (S), Lascar or Creole (Sey). Unmistakable; body greyish, fins faintly pink; distinguishing mark a large elongate dark blotch on side, with a conspicuous red or orange margin. Widespread; in shallow water and shoreline shallows; solitary, but usually more than one fish is seen in the same area at a time; common, juveniles occasionally abundant. Both juveniles and adults, but particularly the former, show rapid and great changes in intensity of body colour, which may vary from dark to very pale grey. This is sometimes dependent on the background the fish is swimming over, sometimes on the emotional mood; body colour is light over sand, dark over seagrass. In juveniles there are several irregular dark blotches across the dorsal surface; these can be intensified at will. The dark blotch on the side of adult fish can also be modulated, and can become so faint as almost to disappear. D X 9; A III 8; L.l. about 45; Tr 6/14; five feeble gill-rakers; Depth about 2.8.

POMACENTRIDAE: Coralfishes, Damselfishes; Dodosi (S); Bouteur (Sey)

The Pomacentridae is a large family of tropical and subtropical fishes with a worldwide distribution; the Indo-Pacific is particularly rich in genera and species. Perhaps the most typical of all families associated with coral reefs, Pomacentrids are mostly small, laterally compressed fish with a distinctive shape; many are brilliantly coloured. As a group they are great opportunists, colonising and exploiting reefs, creek and lagoonal habitats wherever these are even marginally suitable. As a consequence, they are among the first fish to be noticed, and for this reason the family is treated in some detail.

There are five common and widespread genera in the Western Indian Ocean, *Abudefduf, Amphiprion, Chromis, Dascyllus* and *Pomacentrus.* The genera are separated primarily into two groups by Smith (1960) on shape of teeth: in *Abudefduf* and *Pomacentrus* the teeth are flattened and incisor-shaped; in the others they are conical. Within these groups, genera are separated by presence or absence of tiny spines on the operculum or pre-opercle. For most people, these considerations are too technical, and in any case they are of little use as distinguishing underwater characters.

Fortunately, all species are easily identified by coloration, some by habitat preference, and, in many instances, by behaviour.

Territorial behaviour is strongly developed and it seems that most species are resident fishes that tend towards individual or group terri-toriality, at least during a significant part of their lives. The Pomacentrids show a most interesting range in territorial behaviour, from solitary habits, through pairs (these two are not, of course, mutually exclusive) to social patterns where a shoal occupies a group coral territory. Varia-tions on these themes are apparently endless, and there seems at first to be little correlation between coloration or colour patterns and terri-toriality. Konrad Lorenz (1972) thought that there was a correlation, and that the more brilliantly coloured species tended to possess the strongest territorial instincts, but as we shall see this is not necessarily so. What is certain is that the Pomacentrids present an abnormally rich field for studies involving inter-relationships of species, coloration, ecology and behaviour.

One of the most extraordinary of all specialised territories has been chosen by the genus *Amphiprion,* the Clown or Anemone fishes. Pairs of these fish occupy Giant Sea Anemones *Stoichactis,* and live unharmed among the tentacles. This has naturally attracted the attention of scientists; the sequence of events involved in the selection of an anemone has been studied in detail.

The fish swims up to the anemone and allows the briefest of contact between itself and the tentacles, and then withdraws rapidly. This process (called 'acclimation') is repeated again and again over a period of an hour or two, each successive contact lasting slightly longer. Finally, the fish swims into, and nestles among, the tentacles with impunity. Any other kind of fish is immediately trapped by the anemone, paralysed, and devoured. The immunity of the Anemone fish is thought to be due to the mucous covering of the fish which in some way inhibits, most effectively, a sequence of actions on the part of the anemone: the details are not understood.

Anemone fish defend their territories stoutly, and will swim 1 to 2 metres from their home to see off, indignantly, any intruder, including a human. Occasionally, sub-adults are found sharing an anemone with adults, presumably their progenitors. The young of *Amphiprion ephippium* are also to be found in a green soft coral *Sarcophyton,* often sharing this equally dangerous home with the young of *Dascyllus trimaculatus.* At this point the behavioural patterns of these two species diverge widely; *A. ephippium* establishes a territory in a giant anemone, but *D. trimaculatus* subsequently selects a coral or rocky refuge and lives a more or less social, free-swimming life in small groups.

Several other species, while not occupying so remarkable an ecological niche as *Amphiprion,* show equally dogged territoriality, seasonally if not permanently. Outstanding among these are *Abudefduf lachrymatus, A. annulatus, A. xanthozonus, Pomacentrus nigricans,* and *P. sulfureus.* In general, these species do not aggregate into shoals, or only do so rarely (for example, *A. xanthozonas*). Individuals or pairs select a territory, within which is a home site, and they will defend this area against all comers. Intensity of aggression increases from the periphery of the territory inwards. These species are found in different habitats: *A. xanthozonus* and *A. annulatus,* for example, seem happier among coral debris, and it is in rock-strewn areas that they are most often encountered.

Several species occupy group territories: two of the more outstanding examples being *Dascyllus aruanus* and *D. reticulatus.* These two species occupy clumps of stagshorn coral; often every available site within a coral is occupied, and hence the 'territory' is little larger than the fish itself.

At least one species of Damselfish, *Chromis caeruleus,* occupies a similar 'social' territory as juveniles only. Adults leave the nursery area and often aggregate into vast shoals around the periphery of coral reefs.

Finally, there are several species which appear to have lost most territorial instincts and which are normally encountered, swimming freely, a short distance from protective cover. The most common and best known among these is *Abudefduf sexfasciatus,* the Sergeant Major; others include *A. sparoides, A. saxatilis* and *A. septemfasciatus.*

Seasonally, many species aggregate in enormous numbers. I have seen countless thousands of *Chromis dimidiatus* swimming a short distance away from the coral slope at Kisiti Island, Kenya. The reasons for the occurrence of these vast shoals are not known, but one would hazard the guess that they are determined by a coincidence of a superabundance of food and breeding behaviour.

Pomacentrids feed on copepods (Crustacea) and other minute animals and plants. Occasionally larger matter, such as jellyfish and algae, are ingested.

Amphiprion ephippium 12 cm.
See Colour Plate 8, No 4; adults variable, but mostly with black body, white or bluish-white vertical bars, orange fins, whitish-yellow tail fin. One of the two common species of Anemone fish found in the Giant Sea Anemone *Stoichactis*. Juveniles with orange snout, black stripe across eye, then two alternating whitish and black bars; base of tail orange, large black blob covering most of rounded caudal fin; also found in the green soft coral *Sarcophyton,* sharing this home with the juveniles of *Dascyllus trimaculatus* (see p 00). D X-XI 15-17; A II 14-15; P2, 15-16, 1; upper L.l. about 40; gill-rakers 12-13; Depth about 2.0.

A. akallopisos 8 cm.
See Colour Plate 9, No 1; body uniform light orange; a median white bar from snout along top of head. Common, often abundant, in Giant Sea Anemones *Stoichactis*. D IX 17-20; A II 12-13; P2, 14, 1; upper L.l. 37-42; 12-13 gill-rakers; Depth about 2.4.

Abudefduf sexfasciatus 18 cm. Punda Milia (S), Bouteur Carreaux (Sey).
See Colour Plate 9, No 2; five vertical black bars on silvery, bluish body; tail with black bar along each lobe, the distinguishing field mark. Often in vast numbers, in loose shoals. D XIII 12-13; A II 12-13; P2, 16, 1; upper L.l. 19-21; gill-rakers 15; Depth 1.9.

A. dicki 10 cm.
See Colour Plate 9, No 3; body beige, lilac head and chest with orange-apricot tail; black vertical bar between soft dorsal and anal fins. Usually solitary, apparently territorial. D XII 16-17; A II 14-15; P2, 14,2; upper L.l. 20-23; gill-rakers 13-14; Depth about 1.8.

A. saxatilis 25 cm.
See Colour Plate 9, No 4; one of the largest of the Damselfishes; five vertical black stripes on silvery body; dorsal areas between stripes orange-yellow. Juveniles in small schools in reef and shore pools; adults free-swimming, solitary or sometimes in small loose aggregates around coral, piers or wrecks. D XIII 12-13; A II 12-13; P2, 15-16, 1; upper L.l. 20-21; gill-rakers 18-19; Depth 1.7-1.9.

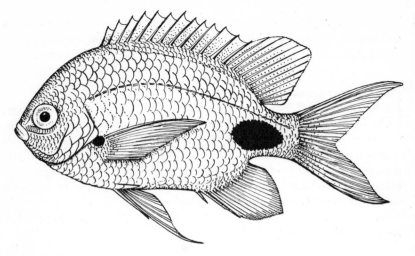

Abudefduf sparoides

A. sparoides 14 cm.
Easily recognised; silvery, with black mark on pectoral axil; black blob
on flank. Usually solitary, mostly seen free-swimming a short distance
from coral. According to Smith (1960), not known outside the Western
Indian Ocean. D XIII 13; A II 12; P2, 15, 1; upper L.l. 20-21; gill-
rakers 18-19; Depth 1.8-2.0.

Abudefduf annulatus

A. annulatus 6 cm.

Whitish, five black rings around body as illustrated, ends of soft dorsal, anal and most of caudal fin orange. In shallow water among coral and rock debris and weeds, solitary, strongly territorial. D XIII 12; A II 12-13; P2, 15, 1; upper L.l. 17-18; gill-rakers 9-10; Depth about 2.0.

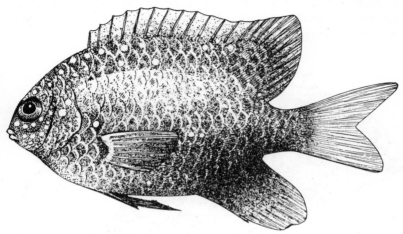

Abudefduf lachrymatus

A. lachrymatus 10 cm.

Brown to dark brown, orange caudal fin, with numerous small iridescent blue or blue-green spots; unmistakable. Very strongly territorial, often aggressively so. D XII 16-17; A II 13-14; P2, 15-16, 2; upper L.l. 19-21; gill-rakers 12-13; Depth 1.9.

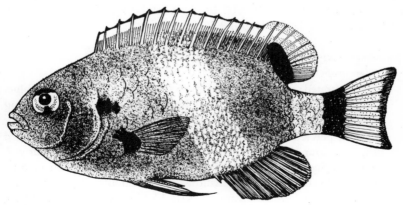

Abudefduf xanthozonus

71

A. xanthozonus 7 cm.

Light brown, median oblique lighter-coloured zone across body; soft dorsal and caudal yellow-orange; ocellus, with iridescent blue margin, at base of soft dorsal, black bar at base of caudal fin. In shallows, often among coral debris; differences in behaviour recorded, possibly related to breeding: some populations appear solitary and territorial, others aggregate into small loose shoals. D XIII 12; A II 11-12; P2, 14, 1; upper L.l. 17-18; gill-rakers 12; Depth about 2.5.

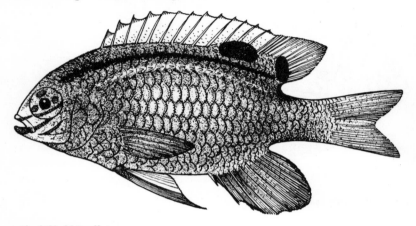

Abudefduf biocellatus

A. biocellatus 7 cm.

Orange-yellow to golden; distinguishing mark a brilliant iridescent blue dorsal stripe from snout along back to end of dorsal fin; two black ocelli, as illustrated; mostly in shallows, or in reef pools; occurs in twos or threes, never observed in shoals. D XIII 10-13; A II 11-12; P2, 16, 1; upper L.l. 17-18; gill-rakers 12-13; Depth 2.5-2.7.

Allied species:

    A. melanopus 8 cm.

    Not illustrated; upper part of body yellow, lower part brilliant blue, the division between these colours being fairly abrupt and following a diagonal from snout, through eye, to tip of soft dorsal fin. Lower edges of pelvic and anal fins black. A vivid and exquisitely coloured fish, in colour the reverse of the equally exquisite *Pomacentrus pulcherrimus* (See Colour Plate 11, No 1), which is dark brilliant blue above and yellow below. In shallows and reef pools; widespread, but apparently nowhere abundant. D XIII 13-14; A II 12-13; P2, 14-15, 1-2; upper L.l. 15-17; gill-rakers 13; Depth 1.7.

A. septemfasciatus 23 cm.

Not illustrated; silvery, with seven vertical yellowish bars; caudal lobes pointed. *A. sordidus* is similar to *septemfasciatus* in that it has six vertical yellowish bars on a silvery-grey background, but the caudal lobes are rounded, not pointed and there is an ocellus on the peduncle behind soft dorsal. D XIII 13; A II 12-13; P2, 16, 2; upper L.l. 21-22; gill-rakers 15; Depth 1.8.

Dascyllus aruanus 8 cm. Banded Humbug (Q).

See Colour Plate 10, No 2; four broad vertical black bars on white; leading edges of pelvic fins brilliant blue. About and among living staghorn coral, in which it is territorial, each member of the group inhabiting the coral and each having a limited home. D XII 12-13; A II 12-13; P2, 15-16, 1; upper L.l. 16-18; gill-rakers 16-17; Depth about 1.6.

D. reticulatus 7 cm.

See Colour Plate 11, No 3; two vertical black bars on white, as illustrated; dorsal fin spines may be brilliant blue. (Smith (1960) stresses that this species is variable, some communities having whole body dark, with white tail.) Mostly about coral, in deeper water; often occurring in same reef area as *Dascyllus aruanus*. D XII 15-16; A II 14; P11, 18, 1; upper L.l. 18-19; gill-rakers 18-19; Depth about 1.6.

D. trimaculatus 13 cm.

See Colour Plate 10, Nos 3 and 4; juveniles jet black, with three vividly contrasting white spots, one in front of head, and one on each side of body below dorsal fin. Adults pale pinky-brown; white spots fade, but are retained. Young mostly but not invariably in green soft coral *Sarcophyton,* which they often share with young of *Amphiprion ephippium.* Adults common, not associated with anemones or soft corals but free-swimming, generally in small loose aggregates, near coral or rocks. D XI-XII 15; A II 13-14; P2, 17, 1; upper L.l. 18-20; gill-rakers 16-17; Depth about 1.5.

Chromis caeruleus 8 cm.

See Colour Plate 10, No 1; body uniformly turquoise blue; social, both juveniles and adults always in shoals. Juveniles occupy a coral in much the same way as *Dascyllus aruanus*; when alarmed the entire shoal disappears into the coral. Adults free swimming, but never far from coral. This species may be confused with *Pomacentrus pavo,* which also occurs in small shoals, and is also turquoise. *P. pavo,* however, has a black spot at shoulder, above pre-opercle, *C. caeruleus* does not. D XII 9-10; A II 9-10; P2, 15, 1; upper L.l. 16-17; gill-rakers 20; Depth 2.1.

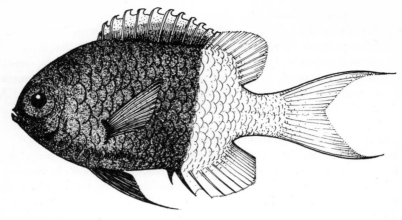

Chromis dimidiatus

C. dimidiatus 7 cm.
Unmistakable; front half of fish dark brown, hind part white, with sharp dividing line between the colours. In small shoals, but occasionally observed in vast numbers. D XII 12-13; A II 12-13; P2, 13, 2; upper L.l. 15-16; 20 gill-rakers; Depth about 2.0.

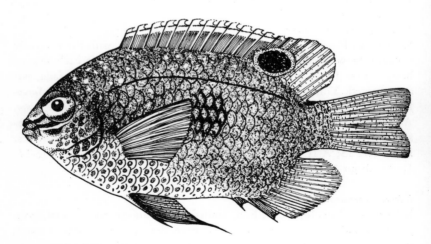

Pomacentrus tripunctatus

Pomacentrus tripunctatus 11 cm.
Colour variable, but most East African specimens appear orange; black spot with brilliant blue margin at the base of last dorsal fin spines and

small black spot at shoulder. About coral, more especially where there are small algal and other growths; solitary or in pairs, territorial. D XIII (XII-XIV) 13-15; A II 13-15; P2, 14, 1; upper L.l. 15-18; gill-rakers 17-19; Depth 1.9-2.2.

P. pulcherrimus 9 cm.
See Colour Plate 11, No 1. Brilliant iridescent dark blue above, orange yellow below; tail orange-yellow. In twos and threes, or small shoals, occasionally large shoals encountered (especially in Seychelles). In reef pools, reef shallows, or around corals. D XIII 14-15, rarely 13; A II 15-16; P2, 14-15; 1; upper L.l. 17-18; gill-rakers 14; Depth 2.4.

P. sulfureus 10 cm.
See Colour Plate 11, No 3. Entire body bright yellow, black mark at pectoral axil. Solitary, abundant about dense coral in deeper water. D XIV 13(14); A II 14(15); P2, 14, 2; upper L.l. 17-18; gill-rakers 13-14; Depth 2.0.

Allied species:
    P. pavo 12 cm.
    Not illustrated; brilliant iridescent blue-green; small black spot at shoulder. In certain incident lights blue, in others green. In small shoals about coral. D XIII 13-14; A II 13; P2, 13-14, 1; upper L.l. 16-17; gill-rakers 15; Depth 2.2-2.3. (See *Chromis caeruleus*, p 00).
    P. taeniurus 9 cm.
    Not illustrated; dark green; pectorals, hind parts of soft dorsal and anal, and caudal fins contrasting yellow. Caudal lobes pointed, filiform, upper often longer. In small shoals, often some distance from protective cover. D XIII 11; A II 10-11; P2+14+2; upper L.l. 17-18; gill-rakers 14-15; Depth 2.3.
    P. nigricans 12 cm.
    Not illustrated; drab brown often with broad paler area across middle of body. Pectoral axil and base of last dorsal rays black. Caudal lobes rounded, body plump. Solitary, strongly territorial, in coral and rock debris. Abundant in many localities; widespread throughout Western Indian Ocean and much of the Indo-Pacific. D XII 15-16; A II 12-13; P2, 15-16, 2; upper L.l. 18-20; gill-rakers 12-14; Depth 1.8-2.0.

LABRIDAE: Wrasses, Rainbowfishes; Pono (S)

The Labridae are close relatives of the Parrotfishes, and these two families are placed, by some authorities, in the order Pharyngognathi, or pharynx-jaws. The name refers to a most characteristic dentition; in both families the lower pair of pharyngeal teeth are united, forming a distinctive triangular Y-shaped bone. This unit normally bears large molars or granular 'teeth', used for crushing corals and molluscs.

The Wrasses are separated from the Parrotfish by the arrangement of the teeth in the jaws. In the Wrasses, the teeth are mostly normal, incisor-like or caniniform, and often project forwards. While in the Parrotfish the outer teeth are usually completely fused together to form a parrot-like beak.

Body shape varies from deep and compressed to elongate and cylindrical. Most species are small or medium-sized (15 to 30 cm), but others attain great size and weight. Some swim with sinuous grace, others with distinctive paddle-like beats of the pectoral fins. Many labrids sleep at night, burying themselves in the sand. The feature of wriggling into sand is used by several species as a means of escape when harassed by predators.

Wrasses are brilliantly coloured fish, and the colour patterns of many species are almost impossible to describe. The common reef-dwelling species are illustrated in colour; difficulties in colour description will be appreciated by referring to Colour Plate 16.

Many species show great changes in colour and colour patterns between juveniles and adults. Good examples of this are found in the genus *Coris*. Juveniles are found in the quieter areas of the lagoon and in deeper reef pools; adults are wide-ranging and occur generally about the reef and lagoon. Two juvenile forms are illustrated, *Coris formosa* (see Colour Plate 16, No 9) and *C. angulata* (see Colour Plate 11, No 4). The adult of *C. formosa* is illustrated in Colour Plate 12, No 1; that of *C. angulata* is brownish, without any spectacular markings.

The juveniles of most of the common genera (*Stethojulis, Halichoeres, Thalassoma*) occur in reef shallow pools, where they make up a considerable proportion of the population of small fish. They are mostly greenish, and flash around the pools when alarmed, with characteristic rapid changes of direction.

Of all the many species of Labrids, the Cleaner Wrasses, *Labroides dimidiatus* (see Colour Plate 12, No 4), are possibly the most interesting. They have highly specialised feeding habits, being symbiotic 'cleaners' which remove external parasites and fungal infections from the bodies of other host fish. They also clean the wounds of their hosts by removing scar tissue.

Cleaner Wrasses are aggressively territorial, and within their territory is a well-defined cleaning station. It is here that host fishes come to be cleaned; often there is a rock or coral in or adjacent to the cleaning station, which acts as a landmark. The young, learner Cleaner Wrasse has a special invitation dance, which consists of shimmying, undulating movements.

It seems that with more experienced fish, the undulating dance is performed less frequently. The host fish often solicits cleaning; and, on being cleaned, adopts various stationary, often 'head up', postures. It also seems that the host fish goes into a trance while the Cleaner browses over its scales and fins; frequently the gill chamber is opened and the Cleaner enters this, and even the mouth of the host.

Their usefulness in a fish community is obvious. Within the community, there are families which seem to make more of a habit of being cleaned than others, and these also seem to be preferred hosts. Such families include Parrotfish, Surgeon fish, Damselfish, Snappers, Triggerfish, and others.

Within the territories of Cleaner Wrasses apparently two social organisations may occur. In the first, adult fish live in pairs, presumably male and female. In the second, more complex social structure, there is one male with a harem of three to six mature and several immature females, living within the territory of the male. The male dominates all members of his harem; larger, older females dominate smaller ones, and there is a linear hierarchy. When the male dies, or is removed, within hours the dominant female changes her behaviour to that of a male, and in two to four days sex-reversal is complete. The linear hierarchy continues to operate, with the female originally second in line moving up to become the dominant first lady, and so on.

It seems that scattered about in the ovaries of females are small areas which contain sperm; normally, these are inhibited from developing and the individual remains a fully functional female. Death or removal of the male means that the female is no longer dominated, and the tendency to change sex is no longer suppressed. The reason for this extraordinary phenomenon of sex-reversal is not fully understood, but it seems that it works towards maintaining a population best adapted to local conditions.

Labroides dimidiatus Adults 6 to 10 cm.
See Colour Plate 12, No 4. Body elongated; light blue, with a longitudinal black stripe through eye to tail. Very young fish (1 to 2 cm) jet black except for blue stripe along body; juveniles (2 to 3 cm) have coloration similar to adult, extent of blue increasing with age. In sub-adults the belly is often pale pink. All stages show territoriality. D IX 10-11; A III 10; L.l. 50-53; Tr 5/12; six gill-rakers; Depth 4.3-5.0. The closely related *L. bicolor* (10 cm) is black with bright yellow tail; yellow extending forwards to include area between soft dorsal and anal fins. *Aspidontus tractus* (see page 88) has mimicked the Cleaner Wrasse *dimidiatus* and close inspection is necessary to distinguish the two species.

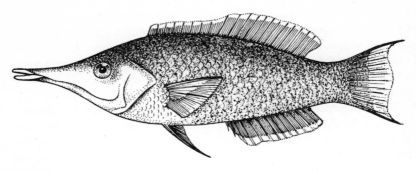

Gomphosus caeruleus

Gomphosus caeruleus 25 cm.
Extreme development of mouth and jaws to form a tubular snout; known for this reason as the Bird Wrasse; unmistakable; swims with paddle-like beats of pectorals. There are two colour forms of this species, one dark blue with green edging to the causal fin, *caeruleus,* the other greyish, *varius*. These are often ascribed to different species, but *varius* is now thought to be the female of *caeruleus*. D VIII 13; A III 11; L.l. 26-30; Tr 3/10; 14 gill-rakers; Depth 3.5-3.8.

Halichoeres centriquadrus 20 cm.
See Colour Plate 12, No 2. D IX 10-11; A III 11-12; L.l. 26-28; Tr 4/9; 13-14 gill-rakers; Depth about 3.0.

H. kawarin 10 cm.
See Colour Plate 16, No 1. D IX 11; A III 10-11; L.l. 28; Tr 3/7; 12 feeble gill-rakers; Depth about 3.25.

H. scapularis 13 cm.
See Colour Plate 16, No 2. D IX 11; A III 11; L.l. 27; Tr 3/9; 12 gill-rakers; Depth 3.25.

Adult colour patterns as illustrated in the colour plates. *H. centriquadrus* and *H. scapularis* are both common, mostly around sandy areas near corals; both burrow into sand. *H. kawarin* is more frequently encountered in and around sea grasses and sea weeds; less common.

Cheilio inermis 30 cm.
Body elongated, pointed snout. At least two colour forms, green and brown; preferred habitat is sea grass meadows in lagoonal areas where it may be abundant. D IX 13-14; A III 11-12; L.l. 45-50; Tr 5/12-14; gill-rakers 17-20; Depth 7.0-8.0.

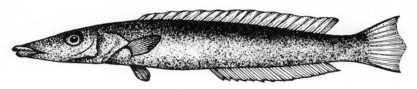

Cheilio inermis

Anampses meleagrides 25 cm.
See Colour Plate 16, No 3; yellow tail and pectoral fins conspicuous.
Both *A. twisti* and *A. caerulopunctatus* are similar. *A. twisti* has lower
half of face yellow; tail orange, with blue spots; two ocellar spots with
blue margins, one at end of dorsal and one at end of anal; *A. caerulopunctatus* is entirely dark with blue spots on body and tail, blue lines,
radiating more or less about eye, on head. For *caerulopunctatus*: D IX 12;
A III 12; L.l. 28-31; Tr 5/11; 12 gill-rakers; Depth about 2.8.

Cheilinus trilobatus Adults to 60 cm.
See Colour Plate 16, No 4. Three distinct lobes to tail most conspicuous,
also red spots on face. D IX 10; A III 8; L.l. 14-16+7-8; Tr 2/6; 5-6
short gill-rakers; Depth about 2.5. There are several species of *Cheilinus*
in the Western Indian Ocean, of these *C. fasciatus* is also fairly common.
C. fasciatus has similar head coloration to *trilobatus,* but the body has a
series of alternate light and dark vertical bars, about six of each.

Coris formosa 30 cm.
See Colour Plate 12, No 1 (adult) and 16, No 9 (juvenile, 5 cm). First
dorsal spine of adults elongated, often conspicuous. Juveniles of a closely
related species, *C. africana,* are very similar to those of *C. formosa*; the white
areas on the body are less extensive. Adults of *africana* are dark, with
brilliant green facial bars; unlike *formosa* they do not have black spots
on their bodies, nor orange on the head. Juveniles solitary, in reef pools
and quieter areas of lagoon, or about coral; adults generally about reef
or lagoon. For *C. formosa*: D IX 12; A III 12; L.l. 77-80; 9-10 short gill-
rakers; Depth about 3.0.

Coris angulata Juvenile 13 cm.
See Colour Plate 11, No 4 and text p 00. D IX 12-13; A III 12; L.l. 62-66;
Tr 9/24; 11-13 gill-rakers; Depth about 3.0.

Lepidaplois axillaris 13 cm.
See Colour Plate 12, No 3; in and about corals. This genus is well-
represented in the Western Indian Ocean, and most species are reddish or

brownish in colour, with two or more conspicuous black spots on head and body. D XII 10; A III 12; L.l. 28; Tr 4/10; 10 gill-rakers; Depth 3.0-3.5.

Thalassoma hardwicki 15 cm.
See Colour Plate 16, No 5. D VII-VIII 12-14; A III 11; L.l. 26-30; Tr 3/9; 16 gill-rakers; Depth 3.0-3.5.

T. hebraicum 20 cm.
See Colour Plate 16, No 6. D VIII 13; A III 11; L.l. 28; Tr 3/10; 13 gill-rakers; Depth 3.25-4.0.

T. lunare 24 cm.
See Colour Plate 16, No 7. D VIII 13, A III 11; L.l. 27; Tr 3/9; 10-12 gill-rakers; Depth 3.5-4.0.
   Colours as illustrated. All three species common, shy, extremely difficult subjects for the photographer. Distinctive marks are black dorsal bars on greenish body in *hardwicki*; lunate yellow tail and short reddish vertical lines on body in *hebraicum*; oblique yellow bar, as illustrated, in *lunare*. The latter species, especially, swims with a curious paddle-like beat of the pectorals. Habitat generally about reef and corals, or near rocks in lagoons.

T. amblycephalus Adults (=*Thalassoma melanochir*) to 16 cm.
The distinctive juvenile colour pattern is illustrated: upper parts black, lower half white or light-coloured. Juveniles common, often abundant, in small shoals, always near coral or rocks, in quieter areas of reef or lagoon, or in reef pools. Adults similar in shape to *hebraicum* and *lunare*; each scale with a dark purple vertical streak, tail reddish. Blue-edged black horizontal stripe from eye to operculum and another obliquely from angle of mouth to lower angle of pre-opercle.

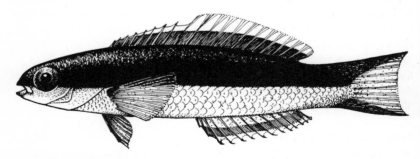

Thalassoma amblycephalus

Stethojulis axillaris 10 cm.
See Colour Plate 16, No 8. Upper half of body conspicuous light green. *Stethojulis albovittata* is another common species; body brownish-red above, whitish beneath, three horizontal bright blue lines along length of fish from head to tail. These small brilliantly coloured Wrasses are common, often abundant, in reef pools and in lagoonal shallows, especially near areas of seagrass. For *axillaris*: D IX 11; A II 11-12; L.l. 27; Tr 3/9; 16-18 gill-rakers; Depth about 3.0.

SCARIDAE: Parrotfishes, Kwangu (S), Pono (S), Kakatoi (Sey)

The Parrotfishes are among the easiest of all reef fish to recognise, and perhaps the most difficult to name with certainty. I have approached the species of this family with great caution, illustrating only two. At the moment the position regarding species names is uncertain; recent studies have shown that in many instances two separately described species are in fact the male and female, or juvenile and adult, of a single species. In addition to this, they are differentiated mainly on coloration, and a written description of the colour patterns is beyond my limited powers. Finally, they are exceedingly wary and, like the Wrasses, are difficult for the photographer.

Parrotfish have robust bodies with fairly large scales, those at the base of the tail being particularly large. The most distinctive difference between them and their close relatives, the Wrasses, is in their dentition: the teeth in Parrotfish are fully united to form a strong, smooth parrot-like beak.

This strong beak is used to crop living coral, which is crushed by the pharyngeal mill of the upper and lower sets of fused pharyngeal teeth. The coral polyps, the major item of the diet, are ingested, the ground powdered coral itself being passed through the gut. Parrotfish are therefore a destructive element of some magnitude in coral reefs; the attractive bright, white coral beaches, on the other hand, receive much of their bulk from the gut of Parrotfish.

The noise of Parrotfish feeding on coral is familiar to most divers; a shoal feeding makes a great deal of noise, as they scrape the hard coral surfaces with their teeth. The scrape marks can be seen very clearly on the surfaces of the larger, rounded corals.

Scarus sordidus 95 cm. (synonyms *Xanothon margaritus* for juveniles and immatures; *Xanothon bipallidus* and *Scarus purpureus* for adults).
Juveniles and immatures common in lagoons: pattern most distinctive, as illustrated. Adult coloration shown in Colour Plate 13, No 1; green, with purple blotches or edges to rear of body scales; upper part of head

81

with bold pattern of purple lines, cheek and caudal area green. Dorsal and anal fins with broad reddish line. D IX 9-10; A III 9-10; L.l. 18+7; Tr 1/6-7.

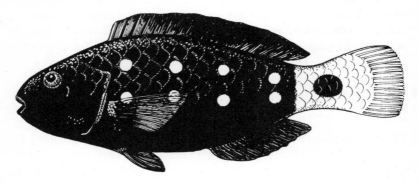

Scarus sordidus

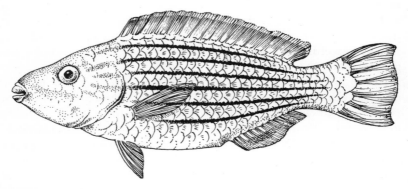

Scarus frenatus

S. frenatus 50 cm. (Synonym *Scarus sexvittatus*)
Colour may be either green or reddish-brown, but both of these colour forms have six blackish lines along the length of the body. Common about coral gardens. D IX 10; A III 9; P2, 12; L.l. 18+7; Tr 1/6; 28 gill-rakers.

Allied species:
    S. ghobban (synonym *S. apridentatus*) 100 cm.
    Not illustrated; is common about coral, mostly in deeper water. Colour mainly greenish-blue, with orange edges to rear of scales; dorsal and anal fins orange. D IX 10; A III 9; P2, 13; L.l. 18+7; Tr 1/6.

Leptoscarus vaigiensis 30 cm.

Not illustrated; is common, often abundant, and is atypical in that its habitat is mainly among the seagrass meadows of the lagoons. It is usually blotched brown to olive-green in colour, lighter beneath, with many distinctive small bluish spots. D IX 10-11; A III 8-10; L.l. about 25; Tr 2/6; 7-9 gill-rakers; Depth 3.5-3.8.

MUGILIDAE: Grey Mullets; Mkizi (S)

The Grey Mullets are readily recognised by their shape, by the two separate dorsal fins (the first always of four spines) and by the position of the pectoral fins, which are characteristically set high on the body, near the upper limit of the operculum. The head is flattened, and the mouth small, teeth being minute or absent; food consists mainly of vegetable matter. Inoffensive and timid, they are mostly grey in colour, and are found in surface waters of creeks and lagoons. The young are frequently encountered in rocky tidal shoreline pools. They are related to the Barracudas.

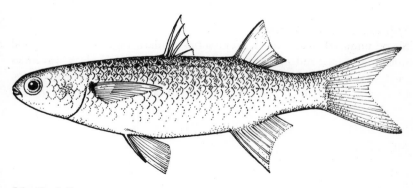

Mugil seheli

Mugil seheli 100 cm. Blue-tail Mullet; Mkizi Burasi (S).
Body grey, tail blue. In small shoals, especially in creeks and lagoons. D IV+I 8; A III 9; 33-36 scales; Tr 13; Depth about 5.0.

SPHYRAENIDAE: Barracuda; Tengezi or Mzio Papa (S)

The Barracudas are included mainly because juveniles and sub-adults are fairly common in shoreline and reef pools, in lagoons, and especially in creeks. They are a supreme example of a predator: the body is torpedo-shaped, designed for bursts of great speed; the mouth is large, with an array of backwardly-inclined, vicious teeth. The lower jaw is longer than the upper.

The whole aspect is slightly sinister and menacing, and most people take careful note of the movements of larger specimens, especially when these are encountered in shoals of twenty or more. They are inquisitive, and will follow a diver for long distances. Barracuda apparently have a bad reputation for aggressiveness in the Caribbean, but this does not seem true of the species in the Western Indian Ocean. Larger fish should none-theless be treated with some caution.

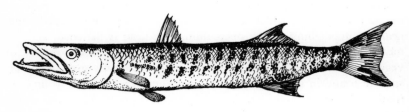

Sphyraena barracuda

Sphyraena barracuda 240 cm.
Shape unmistakable. Silvery grey; series of dark blotches on back and sides; soft dorsal and anal fins with black areas, or mostly black. Juveniles (8-10 cm) in lagoon shallows and shoreline pools; common in creeks. D V+I 9; A I 8; L.l. 75-90; no normal gill-rakers; Depth about 7.0.

SIGANIDAE: Rabbitfish; Tafi (S); Cordonnier (Sey); Spinefeet (Q)

Rabbitfish possess extremely spiny dorsal and anal fins; there is also a forward projecting (antrorse) spine in front of the first dorsal. The body is compressed and ovate; the snout is rounded and is reminiscent of a rabbit's. They are herbivorous, and are most frequently encountered in areas where seagrass meadows and coral formations meet. Often abund-ant; they are extremely good for eating.

Rabbitfish should be handled with care as the needle-sharp, rigid dorsal and anal spines are capable of inflicting painful (but not dangerous) wounds.

At least three Pacific species have a venom apparatus associated with the thirteen dorsal, four pelvic and seven anal fin spines. The spines are grooved along the midline and there are small poison glands. Symptoms induced by severe pricks are said to be similar to those caused by the Scorpaenidae, but this does not seem to be true of the Western Indian

Ocean species. Pricks are mildly painful, but the pain is localised, and soon passes without any swelling or other effects.

Siganus oramin 30 cm. Rabbitfish, Tafi (S) Cordonnier Brisant (Sey).
See Colour Plate 13, No 2. Brownish, with many small but conspicuous rounded blue spots. Abundant in seagrass meadows adjacent to coral heads. D I+XII-XIII 10; A VII 9; Pelvic 1+3+1; 18 gill-rakers; Depth 2.5.

Allied species:
> *Siganus stellatus* 30 cm.
> Less frequently encountered. Brownish, with very numerous smaller dark spots over entire body.

GOBIIDAE, ELEOTRIDAE, BLENNIDAE and SALARIIDAE: Gobies; Sleepers; Blennies and Rockhoppers

These four rather large families, containing between them well over 100 species in our area, have exploited tidal reef and shoreline pools and the shallower lagoons with great success. In these habitats they are common, often abundant, but being adept at concealment, many are unnoticed. They are all small (3-15 cm) carnivorous fish, and are mostly difficult to identify to genus, let alone species, level. Because nothing short of a treatise could do them justice, only a brief introduction to these delightful families is given. Readers whose appetite is whetted should consult Smith and Smith *The Fishes of Seychelles* where the majority of species are splendidly illustrated in colour.

In spite of their small size, many species cover vast areas of the Indo-Pacific, and, taken as a group, they are undeniably highly successful.

GOBIIDAE and ELEOTRIDAE

The Gobies and Sleepers are included in the order Gobioidea; the body is of normal shape, with two separate dorsal fins. Gobies are mainly encountered in tidal shoreline and reef pools; the Sleepers are more frequently found in lagoon and reef shallows, about or near coral. One typical species *Amblygobius albimaculatus* is illustrated on page 86.

These two families are separated mainly on the characteristics of the pelvic fins. In the Gobies, these are fully united or fused together to form a sucking disc; in the Sleepers, the pelvics are separate.

Closely related to Gobies and Sleepers are the charming Mudhoppers (either included in Gobiidae, or placed in a separate family, the Periophthalmidae): their pelvic fins are united at the base only. There is thus a series, Gobies – Mudhoppers – Sleepers, based on degree of fusion of the pelvics. Mudhoppers spend much of their time out of water; their habitat is more or less restricted to tidal mudflats, especially those sheltered by mangrove thickets.

Gobies have sharply defined territories, which are stoutly defended. Several species form close commensal relationships with crustaceans, notably shrimps, the two animals sharing a home.

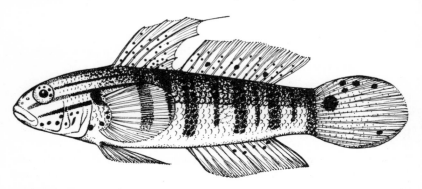

Amblygobius albimaculatus

Amblygobius albimaculatus 15 cm.

Common in sandy localities where there is a light seagrass cover. This fish is greenish above, lighter below, with five vertical dark bars; fins yellowish; caudal fin rounded and bears a conspicuous small black spot dorsally, near peduncle. Always encountered near a hole in the sand, into which it retires when alarmed or harassed. The shape of Sleepers is essentially similar. D VI+I 13-15; A I 12-14; 50-55 scales; Tr 18-20; Depth about 2.8.

BLENNIDAE and SALARIIDAE

The Blennies and Rockhoppers are very much alike in shape, and are all lumped together as Blennies by some authorities. Smith (1965) separates them on dentition: Blennies have normal fixed teeth, which are sometimes relatively enormous and fanglike, while Rockhoppers have freely movable teeth set in the lips.

Not only are they alike in shape, but they share the same habits and habitat; they both favour tidal shoreline and reef pools. They are extremely common in these localities, and hop and skip about with great agility from pool to pool in search of food, or when alarmed.

Blennies and Rockhoppers have elongated bodies, and many species are distinctly eel-like; the dorsal fins are not conspicuously separate (as in the Gobies and Sleepers) and extend along most of the back. The pelvic fins, so much a feature of the Gobies, are much reduced or even absent, and always placed far forward. Rockhoppers often have a tentacle above the eye, and above the nape; many species show sexual dimorphism, the males having a fleshy crest on the head.

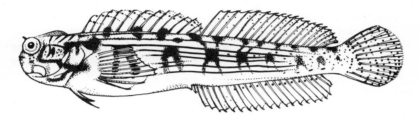

Istiblennius andamanensis

Istiblennius andamanensis 10 cm.
Body elongate, eel-like; pelvics reduced to two small processes, set far forward. Body light-coloured, about six narrow black lines; dorsal and anal fins spotted. Widespread. D XIII-XIV 20-21; A II 20-21; 15-16 apically bispinate gill-rakers; Depth 6.0.

Runula rhinorhynchos

Runula rhinorhynchos 10 cm.
Has an elongate, eel-like body, jet black, with one dorsal and one ventral electric-blue side-stripe, which run the length of the fish. Dorsal and anal fins orange. This attractive fish swims with snake-like grace, and lives in small holes, mostly in coral pools, into which it reverses. (The *Gaterin* in Plate 8 has apparently mistaken the coloration of *Runula* for *Labroides*.) D XI 33-35; A II 31-33; no lateral line visible; Depth 7.0.

Allied species:

The most infamous species of Blenny is the Bogus Cleaner Wrasse, *Aspidontus tractus* (13 cm). This fish has mimicked the true Cleaner Wrasse, *Labroides dimidiatus,* and it is often difficult to distinguish the two without close scrutiny. *Labroides* possesses a petite, typical wrasse-like mouth at the extremity of the snout. *Aspidontus,* in the fashion of Blennies, has its mouth under the face, and this mouth contains rather vicious curved fangs, set in the lower jaw. *Aspidontus* poses as a Cleaner Wrasse; the unsuspecting client approaches, and when the moment is right, *Aspidontus* takes a large bite from fin or scale. This rather villainous behaviour must present at least a partially successful way of life: *Aspidontus* is not common, but it is widespread, and its dark deeds must therefore meet with some success. For *Aspidontus tractus:* D XI 26-27; A II 26-27; Depth 5.0 (compare with formula for *Labroides dimidiatus,* see p 77).

SCORPAENIDAE and SYNANCIIDAE: Scorpionfishes and Stonefish; Chale and Mbevu (S)

The Stonefishes are sometimes lumped with the Scorpionfishes in the family Scorpaenidae; Smith and Smith (1969) treat them separately. The outstanding characteristic they share is the possession of venomous dorsal fin spines.

Scorpionfish, in particular the well-known *Pterois volitans,* are known by a plethora of common names: Scorpionfish, Zebrafish, Lionfish, Turkeyfish, Firefish, Seadragons. I personally prefer the name Scorpionfish, as it at least has the merit of echoing the family name, as well as implying the dangerous attribute of venomous stings.

The Scorpaenidae and the Synanceidae are included in the order Scleroparei or Cataphracti, all species having a bony ridge running across the cheek from gill cover to eye. Many species also have a great number of smaller spines on the head and body; differences in size and arrangement of these have been used in separation of species.

Fishes of a moderate size, they are to be found in shallow water about reefs, among corals, and particularly lurking in coral rubble. Some species are among the most perfectly camouflaged of all; others are brilliantly coloured, attracting attention to themselves both by their colours and by their enlarged filamentous fins. Most species have extremely well-developed dorsal fin spines; these are generally noticeable. In *Pterois* and closely related genera such as *Dendrochirus,* the dorsal spines are separate and greatly elongated, and are covered with a flap of skin. Pectoral fins also have a tendency to be enlarged.

Food consists chiefly of small fish and crustacea, especially prawns.

The enlarged pectoral fins of several species are used to herd small fish into corners, where they are snapped up in sudden lunging gulps. When concealed in rocky clefts, a favourite retreat, the ends of the fins of *Pterois* are so arranged as to be visible and to resemble prawns; they may also thus be used as lures or decoys.

In *Pterois volitans,* the twelve dorsal fin spines are long, straight and slender, with a glandular groove extending the length of the shaft. Situated along the middle third of the shaft, in the groove, is the venom gland, which is sheathed in a thin layer of tough skin. Anal and pelvic spines are similarly equipped.

In the Stonefish, the thirteen grooved dorsal spines are short and heavy, with needle-sharp tips. The venom gland is much larger and sausage-shaped, being developed on both sides of the spine; the sheathing skin is thick and tough. These spines penetrate a tennis shoe with ease.

The venom produced by Scorpionfishes and Stonefishes appears to be similar, and varies in degree rather than in quality. Presumably because of the relatively smaller size of the spines and venom glands, Scorpion-fish stings, though very painful, cannot be considered normally as dangerous. The pain continues for at most a few hours, and is apparently more or less localised.

Wounds caused by Stonefish are more dangerous. Because of an almost flawless camouflage, Stonefish are not easily seen, and are likely to be trodden on heavily. The wound is thus likely to be deeper, and a much larger dose of venom will be injected, under pressure. In general, it seems that the pain induced by the venom is initially more significant than the venom itself; in any event **immediate** first aid is essential. The treatment of wounds inflicted by venomous fish is given in Chapter 7.

Pterois volitans 30 cm. Scorpionfish, Firefish, Turkeyfish; Chale or Mchafe (S), Poisson Volant (Sey).
See Colour Plate 13, No 3. Red to brick red, in a series of 24-28 vertical bars, alternating with narrow vertical (paired) white lines or stripes, this pattern (of 4) on face also. Tail, soft dorsal and anal fins with many smallish conspicuous dark spots. Pectoral rays very elongate, filamentous, not joined or connected by membranous skin. Dorsal spines also fila-mentous. Tentacles above eye in juveniles and sub-adults prominent, reduced or absent in larger, adult species. Young similar to adults, paler, common. D XIII 10-11; A III 6-7; P14; 10-11 gill-rakers; Depth about 2.7.

This species is frequently encountered upside down under a coral or rocky overhang; it is also common among clefts in coral. This is one reason why it is most unwise to grope under coral overhangs or among coral debris.

Allied species:

Pteropterus radiata 25 cm.

Not illustrated; deep red to blackish, with eight to nine narrow light lines across body; oblique eyestripe, bordered white; no spots on caudal, soft dorsal or anal fins. Dorsal spines red at base, whitish towards tips. Tentacles above eyes prominent, reddish. D XII (rarely XIII) 11; A III 5-6; P16; Depth about 2.5.

P. antennata 25 cm.

Not illustrated; similar in coloration and pattern to *Pterois volitans,* but tentacles above eye characteristically banded black and white. D XII 11-12; A III 6-7; P17; Depth about 2.5.

Dendrochirus brachypterus 18 cm.

Not illustrated; scarlet or red, with cross bars. Dorsal, caudal and anal red, with dark spots. Pectorals and pelvics orangey or greenish with dark, usually black, bars; dorsal spines filamentous and free, but enlarged pectorals have rays joined by a membrane, and are thus fan-shaped.

Common in coral debris or rocky rubble, in shallows. D XIII 9-10; A III 5.

Synanceichthys verrucosus 35 cm. Stonefish, Bocho; Mberu or Shinda Ndovu (S), Laffe (Sey).

See Colour Plate 13, No 4. Relatively enormous head and foreparts, body tapers to small caudal fin; pectoral fins much enlarged, eyes sub-dorsal, almost on top of head. Coloration perfectly cryptic, brownish or greyish, which blends with the background. Body with warty outgrowths, often with orange and brown markings. D XIII 7; A III 5: P19; 7-8 low spiny gill-rakers.

Usually among coral rubble and rocky debris, from low tide level to deeper water, in shallow channels or crevices, where it lies in wait for its prey. This consists of smaller reef fish such as Damselfish.

Widely distributed throughout the Western Indian Ocean; records of the related *S. horrida* (distinguished from *verrucosus* by presence of teeth on vomer) probably all refer to *verrucosus.*

Other species:

Sebastapistes albobrunneus 8 cm.

Not illustrated; brownish pink with irregular pale yellow blotches on body, fins yellow. Inhabits the interstices of coral only, usually several fish in one coral clump. This habitat is often shared with a species of a related family, *Caracanthus maculatus* (5 cm), Caracanthidae, which is slate-grey, with brilliant red or orange irregular blotches on upper half of squat body.

Both species are widely distributed; the former is common, often abundant, but it is necessary to look carefully within coral for them.

OPHICTHIDAE and MURAENIDAE: Serpent Eels and Moray Eels; Mikunga (S)
With a brief note on Sea Snakes

Serpent Eels and Morays are so snakelike in appearance and movement that a novice to the tropical reefs of the Western Indian Ocean would almost certainly mistake them for snakes. The Serpent Eels, in particular, are very convincingly snake-like. Not only is this celebrated in their family name, which means, literally, snake-fish (*Ophis*, snake, *-ichthys*, fish), but one of the more common species has, as its specific epithet, *colubrinus*. (The word is borrowed from Colubridae, a well-known family of terrestrial snakes).

Both families of eels are, of course, fish: they possess gills and fins, although the latter may be much reduced. Many of the Serpent Eels, and most of the Morays, are endowed with alarmingly good sets of sharp, canine-like teeth. But they are solid teeth, not hollow or grooved fangs; not one species in either family has any venom apparatus associated with the teeth. Bites often turn septic if not treated properly; so do grazes and lacerations from coral.

It is perhaps useful to comment at this point on true Sea Snakes in the Western Indian Ocean. Sea Snakes are, fortunately, apparently very rare in our area; this is particularly true of the coasts of Eastern Africa. In Kenya, for example, there are only three reliable records of occurrence in about fifty years. All three records are of the Yellow-and-Black Sea Snake, *Pelamys platurus*: this suggests it appears as an occasional stray, and is not a resident, at least not of the coral reefs and lagoons. *Pelamys*, in common with the fifty or so known species of Sea Snake, is well-adapted to its environment: the tail is strongly compressed laterally as an aid to swimming. Coloration is very distinctive: black above, yellow below, with a sharply defined margin between the two colours; the tail s conspicuously marked, with black marks on yellow. No Serpent Eel or Moray has this coloration. Length is given as 60 to 70 cm.

Sea Snakes are common in parts of the East, but it seems that an encounter with one along the reefs or lagoons of Africa and the Western Indian Ocean Islands is only a remote possibility.

OPHICHTHIDAE

Body always elongate and snake-like; dorsal and anal fins present, but much reduced, always ending before the tip of the tail, which is hard and pointed; the caudal fin is absent. In the common species the snout is also pointed. *Myrichthys* is most often seen in sandy areas of the lagoon, or hunting among coral or rocky debris, near sand. These fish have the perplexing attribute of being able to move backwards as effortlessly as they move forwards, and can burrow into the sand, using their sharp pointed tails, with great speed. Sand is their preferred habitat, and they are accurately described as sand-dwelling eels. They are all carnivorous, and many are nocturnal.

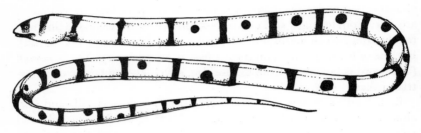

Myrichthys colubrinus

Myrichthys colubrinus 90 cm, but most specimens somewhat shorter. Whitish, with 25-32 narrow black rings around the body; with age black spots may develop between the rings. Commonly encountered in suitable areas, probably because they are more diurnal in habit than other species.

Allied species:
  Myrichthys maculosus 50 cm.
  Not illustrated. Also whitish, with rounded black spots all over body.
  Leiuranus semicinctus 60 cm.
  Not illustrated. Has 24-29 black saddles along entire length. This fish spends most of the daylight hours buried in sand.

MURAENIDAE, MIKUNGA (S)

With few exceptions, much more robust and more heavily built than the Serpent Eels; caudal fin always present, usually distinct round end of tail, and confluent with dorsal and anal fins. The latter fins are sometimes much reduced; they are always encased in thick skin. Mouth large, extending beyond eye; mostly equipped with large conspicuous fang-like teeth.

  They are obviously predatory, and probably mainly carnivorous but will lie curiously motionless in their lairs in daylight hours while small reef fish swim close by. They have a reputation for aggressiveness. While this is overrated, and most individuals, including large ones, do no more than to stare fearlessly and balefully at the intruder, there are occasions when they appear decidedly aggressive. (The subject of the photograph on Plate 14 pursued the photographer (JM) with what can only be described as malicious intent). The answer would seem to be a matter of common sense: Morays are dangerous, and they should not be provoked, under any circumstances. Deep Moray Eel bites should be treated promptly by a doctor, as it is advisable to use antibiotics.

There are numerous authenticated records of the flesh of Morays inducing symptoms of food poisoning when eaten: it seems common sense not to eat them, even when absolutely fresh.

Some species attain great size; specimens of 120 cm are common, and some species attain 240 cm and the thickness of a man's thigh. Genera are separated on several characteristics: some of these are rather technical, others are simpler and include dentition. All the common species are fairly easily distinguished by markings, and are contained in three genera, *Echidna, Lycodontis* and *Siderea*.

Lycodontis favagineus
See Colour Plate 14, No 1. 50-80 cm, but there are records of 240 cm. Markings more or less honeycomb-like; bold, with an aggressive reputation. About reefs.

Allied species:

Lycodontis undulatus 80 cm. (Stated to reach 150 cm).
Not illustrated; teeth conspicuously fanglike, large; jaws not closing completely. Variable in colour, mostly brownish; often speckled in front, irregularly zoned behind. Probably the most common Moray in the Western Indian Ocean.

Echidna nebulosa Average 30 cm, but can attain 70 cm.
Not illustrated. Greyish, with about 23-25 black blotches along sides of body, each blotch with small but conspicuous light-coloured to orangey centres. Common in shallower water in lagoons.

E. zebra 50 cm.
Not illustrated; easily recognised; white to yellow with very numerous narrow black crossbars. Always about reef and coral; not uncommon.

Siderea grisea 38 cm.
Not illustrated; light coloured, usually pinkish, with brown spots or marking; many fine dark spots, arranged in a few irregular lines, on darker coloured head. Common to abundant in creeks where there is suitable cover, especially around fish-traps.

S. picta 60 cm.
Not illustrated; closely related to *grisea,* has body covered with very numerous fine black spots.

BALISTIDAE: Triggerfishes; Kikande, Gona (S); Bourse (Sey)

The Triggerfishes take their name from the 'trigger' mechanism of the anterior dorsal fin, which is reduced to two or three spines only. The large first dorsal spine, always situated some distance **behind** the eye, can be locked erect by the second, smaller, spine. When locked, the first spine can only be released if the second is pulled back, the second spine thus serving as a 'trigger'. These dorsal spines, when depressed, fit into a groove along the back. The larger firmly-locked spine is used by Triggerfish to jam themselves into coral crevices and holes, from which safe position they cannot be removed.

Triggerfish are closely related to the Filefishes (Monacanthidae), which also have a trigger mechanism, but in Filefishes the dorsal spines are situated immediately **above** the eye.

They have a rather deep, compressed, angular body, more robust than the Filefishes, and are encased in a coat of heavy scales. The mouth seems disproportionately small, with well-developed strong teeth, with which they scrape up and crush their food.

Many Triggerfishes are brightly coloured. They are abundant in shallow water around reefs and in the lagoon; their flesh is poisonous.

Rhinecanthus aculeatus 30 cm. Known as the Picasso Triggerfish.
The startling colour design and pattern is unmistakable. See Colour Plate 14, No 3. This species is common in lagoonal areas where there is a sand and seagrass cover to the bottom; they appear to be specially abundant in these localities during incoming tides. D III+24-25; A 22; Depth about 2.0.

Balistapus undulatus 30 cm. Lined Triggerfish.
See Colour Plate 14, No 2; brown; diagonal curved yellow stripes are unmistakable. This species is generally found among coral or rocks, and seems never to be found as far from cover as *R. aculeatus*. Said to bite savagely when removed from the water. D III+26-27; A 23-24; Depth around 2.0.

MONACANTHIDAE: Filefishes; Kikande or Ngana (S); Bourse (Sey)

Similar to Triggerfish, but generally less robust, smaller, body very flattened. Dorsal spines usually situated immediately **above** eye; trigger mechanism as for Triggerfish. The skin is without normal scales; these are reduced to small projections and give the fish a rough, file-like skin.

As in the Triggerfish, the pelvic fins are reduced to a small flap or spine-like process situated on the sharp angle of the belly.

Timid and inoffensive, Filefishes are found among the shelter of reefs and rocks. Mostly drab, but one genus (*Oxymonacanthus*) is brightly coloured and one of the most charming of all reef fish.

Oxymonacanthus longirostris 10 cm. Beaked Leather-jacket (Q).
See Colour Plate 14, No 4; green, with orange blobs; mouth at end of pointed snout. In twos and threes, always about coral.

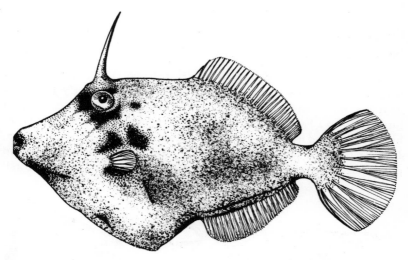

Cantharines fronticinctus

Cantharines fronticinctus 22 cm.
Drab, brownish, with black bars between eyes. Shape typical of the larger Filefish. About coral and coral rubble. D I+32-35; A 29-32. Depth about 2.0.

ALUTERIDAE: Leather-jackets

Leather-jackets are closely related to the Filefishes and Triggerfishes; they too possess a trigger mechanism fashioned from the first two dorsal spines. Their bodies, though flattened, are generally rather elongated; there are no scales and the skin is velvety or leathery. Only two species are mentioned, neither illustrated.
Paraluteres prionurus 10 cm.
Has mimicked the sharp-nosed Puffer, *Canthigaster valentini*.

See text p 100 and Colour Plate 15, No 3, and the two species may easily be confused. *Paraluteres* has a small bump where the dorsal spines are located, and only this gives it away.

Canthigaster is a poisonous genus, and mimicry in this instance presumably confers some immunity from predation.

Osbeckia scripta 60 cm, Figured Leather-jacket (Q).

Not illustrated. Widespread, but infrequently seen. Body elongate, ochre, with brilliant blue short irregular lines and spots. Tail blue, soft dorsal and anal fins yellow; dorsal spine wire-like. D I+43-48; A 46-52; Depth about 3.0.

OSTRACIIDAE: Boxfishes, Cowfish; Sanduku la Bahari (S), Ngombe Maji (S); Coffre (Sey)

The common name of Boxfish is a very apt one. The scales are fused together into a series of often angular plates which encase the body in a hard box, out of which the tail and other fins protrude. The teeth are also fused to form a hard beak. Pelvic fins absent, as are all fin spines. These highly specialised fishes are quite unmistakable; the three common genera, *Lactoria, Ostracion* and *Rhynchostracion* are most frequently encountered in quiet waters of the lagoon and inner reefs, always around rocks or coral.

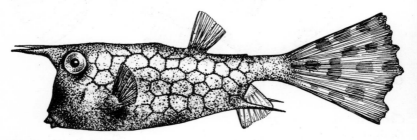

Lactoria cornuta

Lactoria cornuta 30 cm. Cowfish, Ngombe Maji (S).

Most specimens rather smaller than 30 cm; box or carapace squarish in cross-section; caudal fin large. Two forward-projecting large spines in front of eyes, two rearward projecting spines on either side of small anal fin. Body plates conspicuous, more or less hexagonal, each bearing a blue spot. D 9; A 9.

Ostracion tuberculatus Boxfish, Sanduku la Bahari (S).

Attains 35 cm, but usually somewhat smaller fish are seen; carapace squarish in cross-section. Body plates conspicuous, each bearing a round blue spot; body colour of most specimens orange. The juveniles of this species are common, tiny pea-sized Boxfish found sculling among rocks or coral. D 9; A 9.

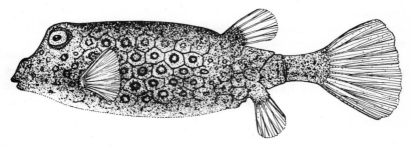

Ostracion tuberculatus

Allied species:

Ostracion lentiginosum 23 cm.
Not illustrated; is very similar to *tuberculatus,* but the body is dark green with numerous light coloured (usually white) spots. The male (=*Ostracion sebae*) is more brightly coloured; back navy blue with white spots; orange or reddish line at upper box angles; pale blue with orange spots below. The female is seen more frequently than the male.

Rhynchostracion nasus
See Colour Plate 15, No 1; 30 cm, body colour orange with dark coloured spots on plates; tail blue with numerous small black dots; snout pinkish. Similar in shape to *Ostracion.*

DIODONTIDAE: Porcupine fish; Chimbera (S); TETRAODONTIDAE: Puffers; Totovu (S); CANTHIGASTERIDAE: Sharp-nosed Puffers; Totovu (S)

These three families of fish are best treated together as they share a number of distinguishing characteristics. They are able to inflate their bellies by gulping in large quantities of water or air to the extent that they become almost spherical; they are all highly poisonous; and their teeth are united to form a solid beak.

The toxic principle in these fish, a powerful nerve poison, appears to be concentrated mainly in the internal organs and the skin; there is no specific medical treatment for puffer poisoning. They are among the most poisonous of all marine creatures, and ingestion may cause rapid and violent death. In spite of this, the flesh and musculature of Puffers are eaten in parts of the Indo-Pacific, notably Japan, where they are known as fugu. Fugu requires extremely careful preparation, and there are specially trained fugu cooks for this purpose. Nevertheless, deaths occur continually, and fugu eating has been described as, at the very best, a statistically biased game of Russian Roulette. Puffers should not be eaten under any circumstances.

Other fish, including the more voracious predators, have learned to leave them severely alone. As a result of being immune from attack, they are fairly bold by nature, and are extremely widely distributed. The heavy fused teeth can inflict deep bites, and most specimens should be handled with care.

DIODONTIDAE: Porcupine fish

The widely distributed Porcupine fishes are so well known that they hardly merit detailed description. They are rather tubby fishes, and are covered with strong spines which normally lie flat against the body. When the fish inflates itself, however, the spines bristle most formidably from the almost spherical body. There are records of inflated porcupine fish being found wedged in the throat of shark.

The two common genera are separated by the nature of the spine roots which are embedded in the skin. In *Diodon,* all the spines are two-rooted, the spine being shaped rather like a flattened Y; in *Lophodiodon* the spines on the body are three-rooted (*N.B.* those on the head are two-rooted).

Diodon hystrix

Diodon hystrix 50 cm.
Porcupine fish; worldwide distribution. Can attain 100 cm. Back greeny-grey, often with velvety brown markings, sides and belly whitish, back

and sides, especially caudal area, covered with black spots. Caudal, dorsal and anal fins usually spotted. Most frequently found at low tide, hiding under rocks or among debris. D 12; A 12.

Allied species:

> Lophodiodon calori 60 cm.
> Not illustrated. Body whitish, with black bars as opposed to spots, one below eye, one in front of, and a larger one behind, the pectoral fin. D 12; A 12.

TETRAODONTIDAE: Puffers, Totovu (S)

Body shape remarkably uniform in all species of the one genus, *Arothon*. See Colour Plate 15, No 2; robust, rather heavy-bodied. Species easily identified by markings and colour. All in quieter waters of reef and lagoon; common in creeks. Single illustration will suffice for all species.

Arothron citrinellus 25 cm.
See Colour Plate 15, No 2. About coral.

Allied species:

> A. *immaculatus* 30 cm.
> Not illustrated; greyish to olive, darker above, body covered in very small rough spines; caudal fin bright yellow, edged black, the distinguishing field character. In quieter waters of lagoon and reef; common in creeks. D 9-10; A 9-10.
> A. *nigropunctatus* 25 cm.
> Not illustrated; olive above, whitish below, with numerous irregularly arranged and shaped smallish black blotches. D 9-10; A 9-10.
> A. *hispidus* 50 cm.
> Not illustrated; greyish body, with numerous small conspicuous light-blue spots.
> A. *stellatus* 100 cm.
> Not illustrated; body greyish, covered in numerous closely spaced black, often star-like, spots. Unmistakable; well camouflaged among coral; largest species. D 10-11; A 10-11.
> A. *meleagris* 30 cm.
> Not illustrated; body blackish, covered with very numerous minute white spots.
> A. *aerostaticus* 20 cm.
> Not illustrated; body orange (but may vary to brown or greenish), with a series of black stripes, sometimes broken; tail spotted. D 10-11; A 10-11.

CANTHIGASTERIDAE: Sharp-nosed Puffers, Totovu (S), Bourse (Sey)

Mostly small and colourful, the Sharp-nosed Puffers are the most common of all the Puffer fishes and at least one species, *Canthigaster valentini,* is nearly always seen about reefs and rocks. The body is rather more flattened than in the other Puffers. Only one genus, *Canthigaster.* They grunt and croak when removed from the water. Body shape typical and constant.

Canthigaster valentini 20 cm.
See Colour Plate 15, No 3; arrangement of black saddles, crossbars and spots characteristic. Eye colour fluorescent green, unmistakable. Common, often in pairs. D 9-10; A 8-9.

Allied species:
> *C. janthinopterus* 10 cm.
> Not illustrated; very dark green, with very numerous, closely-spaced white spots.
> *C. margaritatus* and *C. bennetti,* both 15 cm.
> Not illustrated; are very similar. Both species have iridescent bluish lines around eye, and both have a black ocellar spot with an iridescent blue margin at base of dorsal fin. *C. margaritatus,* however, has numerous blue spots on sides of body and lighter spots on caudal fin; *bennetti* does not.

ANTENNARIIDAE: Toad fishes, Fishing frogs

These small fishes are more common than is immediately apparent, as they are past masters at concealment. Curious lumpy, almost misshapen fish, the pectoral fins are elbowed and resemble minute 'arms'. The mouth is large, and sub-dorsal; they all have a small spine (the first spine of the dorsal fin) on their snouts. The spine ends in a lure which resembles one to several small worms. Concealed among seaweed or algal covered rocks, the fish jiggles the lure enticingly. Small fish are thus attracted, and they are suddenly engulfed into the large mouth. Toad fishes have enormous stomachs, which are capable of holding a fish almost as large as themselves.

One genus only, *Antennarius*; there are several species, all extremely difficult to differentiate as colour and markings are very variable. An outline diagram of *Antennarius* is given above. Formula is D I+I+I+ 11-14; A 7-8.

Antennarius sp.

DASYATIDAE: Stingrays, Shepwe (S)

The Stingrays belong to the order Rajae or Batoidei, in which are included the Electric Rays, Eagle Rays, Manta Rays, Sandsharks, Skates and Sawfishes. With the exception of the Stingrays, Electric Rays and Sandsharks, most members are moderate to deep-water forms, and do not concern us here. The Stingrays are by far the commonest group encountered in tropical reef shallows; much less frequently an Electric Ray or a Sandshark is seen.

In most rays the body is flattened, the pectoral fins are greatly enlarged and wing-like, and are fused along the sides of much of the length of the fish. The resultant disc-like 'body' may be lozenge or diamond-shaped, more or less ovate, or nearly circular. Their gill slits are situated on the underside of the body; there are two well-developed spiracles used in breathing behind the eyes on the back. Teeth are generally flattened and molar like; they burrow into sand and obtain worms, molluscs and crustaceans on which they feed.

There are two common genera of Stingrays, *Taeniura* and *Dasyatis*. In the former the disc is smoothly ovate; in *Dasyatis* it is more or less lozenge shaped or rhombic. The tails are long, and in *Dasyatis* whiplike.

Both species possess one or two serrated, grooved spines, enclosed in a sheath of skin, some distance from the base of the tail: this apparatus

101

is termed the sting. The spine consists of vasodentine, a hard bony material. Along either edge of the spine are a series of sharp recurved teeth, and running along its underside length are two deep grooves. These grooves contain a soft, greyish tissue, and this in turn contains the venom. The grooves and their venom glands or tissue are normally protected by the spine sheath, but the venom glands continue to operate even when the sheath is worn away. Great care should therefore be exercised even when handling a detached spine.

The favourite habitat of both species is warm, shallow water in sheltered small sandy bays, sandy shallows of the lagoon, or sandy areas near shallower reefs; smaller specimens may be found in great numbers in 30 to 40 cm of water a few metres from the edge of the sea. They lie motionless, often half buried in the sand, and it is here, and not in deeper water, that they present the greatest danger.

When a foot is placed on a Stingray disc, the tail is lashed forward in a S-shaped movement and the spine is driven into the area around the foot, ankle, or lower part of the leg. The flesh is either punctured by the sharp tip of the spine, or there is extensive laceration because of the recurved spines. Pain is intense and, if the wound is deep, prompt medical attention should be sought.

The danger of treading on Stingrays in sandy shallows where they are known to be abundant may be eliminated by shuffling the feet along, rather than walking, or by prodding the sand ahead with a stick. Rays are not aggressive, and both these simple precautions will result in their hurried flight.

The spines are used as spear tips in some areas, and classical scholars will remember that Odysseus was slain by such a spear.

Taeniura lymma Blue-spotted Lagoon Ray, Shepwe (S).
See Colour Plate 15, No 4. Body 60 cm wide. Blue spots on yellowish to sandy-coloured ovate disc. Tail longer than body, thickish, never whiplike. Common, often abundant, in warm sandy shallows.

Allied genera:
   Dasyatis uarnak Stingray, Whipray, Stingaree, Shepwe (S).
   Not illustrated; large specimens to 150 cm wide, generally only smaller ones seen. Disc diamond shaped, light sandy coloured, with marbling or spots; tail very long, whiplike. Less common than *Taeniura*.
   Torpedo fuscomaculata Electric Ray, Kiteza (S).
   Not illustrated; attains 45 cm, mostly smaller specimens seen. Disc circular, not ovate or diamond shaped, tail short, caudal fin well-developed, flattened. Body covered with small dark spots, or marbled.

The electric organs lie one on each side of the body, contained in the disc; they are capable of giving a sharp shock, described as the equivalent of that given by a motor car plug lead. The electric organs are used to stun fish prey swimming into the electric field, and not primarily as a means of defence.

7 Potential Hazards of the Reef: Avoidance and Treatment

Under most circumstances, the quiet waters of the lagoon and the sheltered areas of inner reefs are among the more tranquil and safe places of the earth. There are, however, a small number of potential hazards, all of which are avoidable. Avoidance implies recognition, and this chapter is concerned mainly with recognition, awareness, and common sense.

Sunburn

The risk of sunburn is a very real one. Fishwatching is a fascinating and absorbing business and frequently all sense of time is agreeably lost. Two or more hours is a long period to be exposed to the almost vertical rays of the equatorial sun; unless common sense is used, severe sunburn inevitably results. The sun is fiercest from about ten o'clock in the morning until three or four in the afternoon, and it can be equally fierce on cloudy days. For visitors unused to the sun, extreme caution is advised. An old shirt (T-shirts are best) and a hat should be worn, at least until a reasonably protective suntan has been acquired, and it is suggested that Vitamin A tablets are taken **before** exposure.

For treatment of painful sunburn and attendant exhaustion, Vitamin A tablets (either of 25,000 units or 50,000 units) are recommended, one to be taken two or three times a day. In addition, the application of soothing liquids or creams, such as calomine lotion, to the worst affected areas usually affords some relief. If badly burnt and blistered, application of Betnovate or similar preparations is indicated.

Currents

It is generally advisable to have at least some idea of the state and time of the tides, and of local currents. It can be unnecessarily exhausting to have to swim the several hundred metres that were comfortably waded an hour or two before. Currents are not normally a problem in lagoons, but it is as well to know that the vast amounts of water in the lagoon empty through relatively narrow channels, where extremely strong currents may flow during ebb tides. All but the strongest of swimmers would do well to avoid these areas, particularly when alone.

Coral cuts

The most common of all minor injuries sustained in lagoons and on reefs are caused by coral cuts and abrasions. The surfaces of all corals are very sharp and jagged and will cut or graze the skin easily. It is important to treat even the smallest cuts and abrasions, as these are prone to flare into reddened, painful or itchy sores. All coral wounds should be washed thoroughly in fresh water and a mild antiseptic such as mercurochrome applied. More severe lacerations should be thoroughly cleaned of foreign material and similarly treated. If the wounds have not healed in two to three days, antibiotics may be needed and medical advice should be sought.

Coelenterates

In Chapter Two the tiny unique stinging cells of the Coelenterates were described. While the stings of most members of this large class of animals are too mild to be noticed, there are a few species which are capable of inflicting painful, and in one or two cases dangerous, stings.

Perhaps the best known of these is the Portuguese Man-o'-War, or Blue Bottle (*Physalia*), easily recognised by its balloon-like float and blue trailing stinging tentacles. Less commonly encountered are species of the true jellyfishes (the Blue Bottle is not a jellyfish), usually with a jelly-like umbrella which pulsates to keep the animal swimming. Jellyfish come in a great range of colours and sizes, and many species are capable of stinging.

Most jellyfish stings result only in mild (though painful) skin irritations, but there are a few species which are positively dangerous. As far as I am aware, none of the latter have been recorded from the Western Indian Ocean. The dangerous species are the Sea Wasps, Sea Nettles, or Box Jellyfish (*Chironex, Chiropsalmus* and *Carybdea*), mainly found in the Timor Sea and Western Pacific, whose stings may result in death in less than ten minutes. They are all more or less box-shaped, up to fifteen cm across the 'umbrella', and semi-opaque; there is a fleshy arm at each bottom corner of the cuboid body, and each arm branches into tentacles which can trail for a length of five metres. Although the Box Jellyfish are thus distinctive, all jellyfishes should be regarded as dangerous and the utmost care exercised if encountered, either in the water or on the beach.

Should one be stung by a Blue Bottle or jellyfish, it is advisable to leave the water as soon as possible and to apply methylated spirits or alcohol (gin is a passable substitute) to the skin. **Do not in any circumstances apply water.** Alcohol inhibits any further discharge of stinging cells; fresh water induces the batteries remaining on the skin to discharge. If the stings are severe and extensive, medical attention must be sought at the first opportunity, after the immediate first aid application of methylated spirits.

Two other groups of Coelenterates are capable of stinging painfully, though never dangerously. The Stinging or Fire Corals (two species, *Millepora platyphylla* and *Millepora dichotoma*) resemble the true or stony corals but are in fact more closely related to the hydroid Blue Bottle. *Millepora platyphylla* is an upright lobed plate 'coral' which can be recognised by the absence of the individual coral polyp cups: the surface is covered with small (about two mm) conical bumps. *Millepora dichotoma* has a similar though smoother surface. Here the growing ends of the branches divide equally into two branches, each of which in turn again divides equally and symmetrically, and so on. These branches re-unite to give a reticulate, plate-like 'coral' body.

Lytocarpus is a colonial hydroid Coelenterate which grows in upright bunches of delicate white, or brownish-pink, plume-like, feathery tufts, about twenty cm high. Brushing against these results in a fairly painful sting, soon evident as a mildly inflamed rash or weal, but which is otherwise harmless.

In the vast majority of cases Coelenterate stings are localised, even though some, particularly Blue Bottle stings, may be very painful and they may occasionally result in mild shock. In some cases, however, the reaction may be more general. With these, medical attention must be sought; in circumstances where there is no possibility of medical aid, anti-histamine tablets should be taken.

Shells

Cone shells, in our area mainly Geographer Cone *Conus geographus* and Textile Cone *Conus textile* possess a highly developed and efficient venom apparatus. Living cone shells should not be picked up or handled. There is no specific antidote for cone shell stings; in the event of a sting, however, first aid as described for venomous fish stings should be administered promptly and medical aid sought.

Fish with venomous spines

There are two families of bony fish, some species of which are common, which possess dangerous venomous spines. These are the Scorpaenidae, containing the Scorpionfish and Stonefish and a host of smaller species, and the Barbel-eels (Plotosidae). In addition to these are the cartilaginous Stingrays, *Taeniura* and *Dasaytis*.

The individual species have been described in the text, and it is urged that they be memorised. Fortunately they are mostly very distinctive species, and are readily recognised.

It is perhaps unnecessary to warn against handling any of these species, or that they should be treated with the utmost respect, in the water or out of it. The danger from Scorpionfish and Stonefish lies mostly in their habits: fortunately again none of the species is aggressive by nature. Scorpionfish spend much of their time concealed under coral overhangs or in crevices. For this reason, great care should be exercised when gripping a coral or rocky ledge, either when steadying oneself in the water, or when using a coral projection to hold oneself underwater.

Stonefish are rarely seen as their camouflage is near perfect, and they lie motionless. They prefer areas of rocky or coral rubble and debris, where they conceal themselves in small channels or crevices. It is advisable to swim across such areas of the lagoon or reef, if possible; where it is necessary to walk or wade, a path should be selected along sandy or seagrass areas. A stout, shortish stick is a useful aid in punting quietly across the shallower rocky places.

Avoidance of Stingrays has been discussed under the relevant description of the family (p 101).

In the event of being jabbed by the spines of any one of these venomous species, it is essential to leave the water as soon as possible, either onto the reef platform or preferably the shore. First aid consists of immediate immersion of the affected limb (wounds are almost always on hands or feet) in water as hot as the patient can possibly bear, for at least thirty minutes. The reason for this treatment lies in the fact that the venom is largely protein in nature, and proteins are more or less readily denatured by heat. Incisions at the site of puncture to induce blood flow, and sucking the wound in an attempt to remove the venom are not helpful.

Subsequent to hot water first aid, medical attention should be sought. If the possibility of medical help is remote, and if the patient's condition after prolonged hot water treatment remains adverse, a local anaesthetic should be injected at the site of the puncture and just above. The latter is only recommended in the case of deep Stonefish wounds. Scorpionfish stings, though very painful indeed, are not normally dangerous and should normally respond to hot water treatment.

After hot water immersion, the wound should be cleaned and dressed with an antiseptic or antibiotic. It should be remembered, however, that while the primary shock which follows immediately after stinging can generally be coped with by the measures indicated, in some instances secondary shock can be serious and medical attention for all but the slightest pricks is urged.

Fish which can bite

Few species of fish which inhabit the lagoons or inner reefs are capable of inflicting bites. It is not necessary to discuss sharks in detail here, as they cannot be considered a lagoonal animal and are not included in this book. They do not occur inshore of the reef, and I know of no instance, reliable or otherwise, where sharks of any size have been encountered in lagoons. Why smaller shark do not cross the reef at high tide is something of a mystery, but the fact is that they do not. They can therefore be dismissed from the mind of the lagoonal swimmer.

Small shark are sometimes seen in deeper waters of inner reef systems, and the White-Tipped Reef shark *Triaenodon obesus* has been recorded on these more exposed reefs. It seems that the soundest advice, in the most unlikely event of encountering one, is as follows. In that any shark of 1.5 metres or more is potentially dangerous, do not under any circumstances set out to provoke it. Try to suppress the natural urge of panic; if necessary, swim away quietly and purposefully using, if on the surface, the breaststroke not the crawl. The essence, apparently, is to refrain from any erratic movement. Reliable data suggest that sharks are irresistably attracted by jerky or convulsive movements, such as the violent death-shudders of a speared or wounded fish. Swimming movements should therefore relay the exact opposite 'message', which should be one of confident, quiet, rhythmic motion.

Moray Eels and Barracuda, unlike sharks, are lagoon and creek-dwelling species. The former are common, often abundant; the latter of rarer occurrence, at least specimens of any appreciable size. Both species are capable of inflicting nasty bites. It is the height of folly to provoke or to disturb Morays intentionally; do not prod large specimens with a stick, or challenge them with careless and provocative movements of an injudicious flipper. They are most safely observed from a distance. Very rarely, the 'critical distance' may be transgressed, and a Moray may then display aggressively by swimming towards or around the intruder. In these circumstances it is eminently sensible to back down and make an exit, which may necessitate leaving the water. Morays cannot be considered as normally aggressive and will reciprocate respectful treatment.

Barracudas are inquisitive creatures and will often follow a diver for long distances, being particularly attracted, it is said, to bright, shiny objects such as a wrist watch or the chrome on diving cylinders. It is advisable to treat larger specimens or hunting packs with some caution, and to refrain from provoking them.

In the extremely unlikely event of an injury, bites should be thoroughly cleaned, bleeding arrested if necessary, by applying a gauze pad to the wound, under light pressure, and the wound dressed with antiseptics. Seek medical attention if there are any signs of infection, which often occurs with Moray bites.

Sea urchins

Sea urchins are an ever-present, frequently abundant, but minor hazard to the careless fishwatcher. The spines of several species are extremely long, sharp and brittle; they break easily, leaving the tips embedded in the skin. They are almost impossible to remove because of their brittleness. There may be a purplish or blackish discoloration of the skin around the embedded spine tips due to a dye contained in the spines, but this is harmless and should not be a cause for alarm.

Wounds from sea urchin spines, though painful, are not in any way dangerous and normally do not call for any treatment other than the application of a soothing cream. The area around the punctures may be sore and stiff, but most spines are absorbed by the body and healing is uneventful. However, on occasion spines remain embedded and cause secondary infection. Probably in every case of wounds involving several spines, it is worth applying a compress of magnesium sulphate or pawpaw *Carica papaya*. Either the flesh of the fruit should be pulped and applied, or the flesh scraped from the skin and the skin taped onto the wound.

Sea urchins should not be handled. In addition to the likelihood of spine pricks, at least one species *Toxopneustes pileolus* is venomous. This short-spined species lives in shallow water, often along the margins of seagrass meadows, and covers itself with bits of broken shells and small fragments of coral. In between its short spines are small flexible pincer-like seizing processes, the pedicellariae. They are much like a very tiny animated version of ice tongs. The sharp points of the prongs are associated with small venom glands, and these are reported to be dangerous. It is thus unwise to attempt to pick up or handle sea urchins.

This brief essay on potential hazards of the lagoon and reef will, I hope, serve to make fishwatching, a safe pursuit anyway, even safer. With the possible exception of the Stonefish, none of the very few species capable of inflicting wounds or pain can be considered dangerous in any degree and most injuries can be attributed to carelessness. All that is necessary is to be aware of the hazards listed here, to be able to recognise them, and thus avoid them.

8 Underwater Photography

by Ian Took

It is encouraging to note that more and more underwater swimming enthusiasts are forsaking spearguns in favour of the camera. The growth of this rewarding interest has been remarkable over the past few years, and what was once a hobby of the wealthy or adventurous can now be practised by anyone prepared to learn a few basic skills.

A wide choice of underwater photographic equipment is available, and apart from offering a fascinating extra interest to the diver, good underwater photography can be of great value to the scientist and student of marine life. Our knowledge is still very limited on this subject, and while much can be learned from studies of collected specimens and creatures confined in aquaria, nothing can quite replace the value of studies made in the creatures' natural environment. Underwater photography provides a permanent and valuable record of species and their habitats.

This chapter is intended to give the would-be underwater photographer an introduction to equipment and techniques. It is not a step by step guide, but a series of brief discussions based on my own experience. Several books devoted entirely to the subject are readily available and will give the reader more detailed information, but being a relatively new field, there are no hard and fast rules. The newcomer is urged to experiment as much as possible, keeping detailed records. Experience is the best teacher, and this particularly applies to underwater photography.

The photographic illustrations in this book were all taken underwater and are a record of fishes in their natural environment. Most have been taken at close range (30 to 90 cm) because of the small size of most of the fishes described, and also to overcome problems of poor visibility.

Contrary to popular opinion, tropical waters are not always 'gin clear', and visibility can at times be very poor indeed, particularly on coastal fringing reefs where harbours, creeks and river outlets bring down considerable volumes of sediment.

The camera used for the majority of my photographs was a Rolleiflex 3.5F, with or without close-up lenses, housed in an underwater case which I designed and constructed. Depths varied from 3 to 30 metres and in the majority of cases suitably filtered electronic flash was used to obtain as near as possible correct colour renderings.

Cameras for underwater use

A good choice is available and one can either buy a camera such as the 35 mm Nikonos which has been especially designed for underwater use and has the advantages of simplicity and compactness, or one of the custom-made underwater housings which will accept a wide range of cameras, in particular the popular 35 mm single lens reflex.

When considering the pros and cons of various outfits for underwater use, the depth of one's pocket has a considerable influence on the final choice. Any camera is capable of producing an underwater photograph if suitably housed; even the simple box camera or the Instamatic type is capable of producing acceptable results when used in clear and shallow waters.

Reflex cameras, either single or twin lens, are ideal for underwater work and, when fitted in a well designed housing with all necessary controls, are capable of covering virtually all underwater assignments.

The facility afforded by a focussing screen confers a great advantage over those types where distances must be measured or estimated with a consequent risk of error.

Many keen diver-photographers make underwater housings to suit their own cameras; this is well within the capability of the average handyman. Acrylic plastic (Perspex) 10-15 mm thick is probably the most suitable material available. It is easily worked with normal wood and metal working tools and, being transparent, enables all controls and camera settings to be seen at a glance. Wood, fibreglass, brass and aluminium are also commonly used and can all be employed in a satisfactory home-made housing. All one needs are patience and ingenuity, and a modicum of skill.

Problems and phenomena of underwater photography

Photographs taken in apparently crystal clear tropical water sometimes appear foggy. This effect is caused by myriads of tiny suspended particles in the water, and reflection and scatter of sunlight by these causes very low contrast.

While visual visibility can sometimes reach thirty metres, one is limited to photographic distances of only six metres or so, even in these ideal conditions, again because of the low contrast of the whole scene.

Generally speaking, visibility of 12-15 metres would be considered good for photography and will enable clear shots to be taken of anything up to three metres range. Even in dirty water it is still possible to obtain successful close-up photographs if care is taken with lighting. Adapt your technique to the prevailing conditions and you will be pleasantly surprised at the success rate achieved.

Distances underwater are not what they appear. Because refraction of light rays occurs between water and the air inside your camera case, all underwater objects appear to be one-third larger, or closer, than they really are. You cannot, therefore, measure say one metre to an object and transfer this to your camera focusing scale – the object will not be in focus. The camera will see things as you do, and failing a reflex system which will always focus correctly, it is best to estimate distances and transfer the estimate to your camera focusing scale. If you wish to be precise, calibrate a measuring stick, making every three cm marking four cm long and transfer this reading to your camera, i.e. every four cm of actual distance equals three cm on your camera focusing scale.

Needless to say, fish do not take kindly to being prodded with a measuring stick and are unlikely to stay around while you make ready to photograph them. This technique is, however, extremely helpful for photographing inanimate objects or stationary creatures such as starfish, anemones and corals. Wire frames and all sorts of ingenious devices have been used to overcome focusing problems with non-reflex cameras, but reflex focusing offers considerable advantages.

Low contrast is a problem with monochrome photography, but this can be improved by the use of yellow filters or extended development of the film.

With colour photography there is a far more acute problem, namely loss of colour with increasing depth and/or distance. Unfortunately, water is a very effective and somewhat selective filter of light rays. Colours at the long end of the spectrum are the first to be affected and for all practical purposes reds are effectively absorbed through a water path of 3-4 metres. Oranges are next to go, followed by yellows, until at twelve metres or so the colour film is incapable of recording any colour other than a predominant blue or blue/green effect. This can at times give very pleasing results, and will convey the underwater scene roughly as you, the diver, see it, but it is quite unacceptable if you aim to record colour accurately.

Colour-compensating filters (CCR series) can be used to put back some of the missing reds, but are only partially effective and cannot be used successfully below six metres. Beyond this you must use artificial illumination if colours are to be recorded accurately – either flash bulbs, electronic flash or continuous lighting if making cine films.

Techniques

While much useful work can be accomplished by the snorkel diver equipped with only mask, snorkel and fins, the advantages conferred by the use of an aqualung are obvious. It is, however, essential that you have been fully trained in the use of this equipment and that its use has become second nature.

Although tropical waters are warm (23-28°C), some form of protective clothing is advisable for the underwater photographer to provide a barrier against stinging plankton, corals, jellyfish, and other sometimes invisible small creatures that have a habit of picking on the underwater cameraman. A light pair of gloves (household rubber gloves will do) are virtually essential as one is always grasping pieces of coral and rock to steady one's aim, and the unprotected hand is easily cut or grazed. There are other more dangerous and poisonous creatures to be aware of, particularly the almost invisible Stonefish, and care should be taken when approaching Stingrays and the beautiful Scorpionfishes. Treatment of minor and more serious wounds is covered elsewhere in this book.

Once you have spotted a subject to photograph, your approach should be leisurely and quiet. If it is a fish, dive down to the creature's own level and approach as slowly as possible. It is an advantage to be slightly over-weighted if any water movement is evident, as this will give better stability. During the approach, estimate the size of your subject and pre-set the focusing scale on your camera to give the desired degree of reproduction. Other controls should also be pre-set, i.e. aperture and speed. Having done this, you can approach your subject slowly with one eye pressed to the focusing screen or finder, until hopefully the subject is in focus and perfectly framed, and you can trigger the shutter. This ideal situation rarely happens in practice and much time and wasted film is often incurred before an acceptable picture is obtained. If photographing by available light, an exposure meter will give reliable results. A selenium meter is to be preferred, although less sensitive, as some CdS meters are rather colour-selective and can at times give false readings, particularly in deeper waters.

If using flash, it is advisable to carry out a series of experiments and establish your own set of guide numbers for the unit in use. As an approximate guide, you will need to divide the surface guide number by three or four. Positioning of the flash gun is also important, and if possible should not be mounted 'on camera' or in the same housing as the camera. Direct frontal lighting is to be avoided as an unpleasant 'snowstorm' effect can result due to reflection of light from particles suspended in the water. This effect is difficult to avoid entirely, but can be reduced if the flash head is set above and possibly to one side of the camera.

When photographing in close-up, which is necessary for single specimens of most reef fishes, the problem is not so acute and successful pictures can be obtained in water of very low visibility.

Opinions vary as to whether to use flash as a fill-in light to bring out the colours of the main object and allow the natural blue/blue-green colour to form a background, or whether to use flash as the sole source of illumination. Certainly, in deep waters one has to rely on flash as the sole source of illumination and tolerate an inky black background.

Where sufficient natural lighting is available, I prefer to use flash as a fill-in light, selecting an aperture/shutter speed combination to allow full illumination of the main subject only, and yet allow sufficient exposure to give some natural background detail. When working at very close range, i.e. less than sixty cm or so, flash will normally provide the whole illumination. Cameras fitted with focal plane shutters can present problems in well-lit waters, especially with electronic flash where synchronisation is limited to 1/40 or 1/60 second. In certain conditions where the subject is moving, double images can result, the main image from the flash illumination and a faint secondary image from the natural light exposure. This is not a serious or frequent problem, however, and is one that can be largely eliminated if the camera is synchronised at 1/125 second, as at this speed all but the most rapid movement is arrested and sufficient exposure given at average depths to provide background detail.

Almost any film can be used underwater, but as each has its own characteristics it is advisable to experiment with a range of types.

In clear, sunlit waters or with flash, I would suggest starting with one of the medium speed monochrome films (50-200 ASA). They have adequate speed and offer inherently higher contrast and finer grain than the faster films. If conditions are poor, use a medium-fast film of around 400 ASA. A yellow filter can be used to advantage to improve the poor contrast usually encountered, or extended development times can also be used to the same effect, without the loss of film speed that occurs when filters are used. Using a few rolls of film on a trial and error basis, and keeping accurate records of the results, is the best recipe for success. Once you have established a suitable film/exposure/development combination, stick to it.

Regarding colour film, one has the choice of colour negative material which will produce prints, or colour transparency material which can produce both transparencies and prints. For preference, I use medium-speed transparency material (50-64 ASA) for most of my work, particularly as good quality prints can be obtained from colour transparencies, giving one the best of both worlds.

For artificial illumination, either flash bulbs or electronic flash can be used. As a very general rule, blue bulbs should be used for distances up to one metre and clear bulbs beyond. Electronic flash will often need some form of 'warming up' filtration, as colour temperature varies somewhat from unit to unit and only trial and error will decide what filtration, if any, is needed.

For very close distances, 30-50 cm the colour may be acceptable, needing perhaps a light red filter, for shots in the 50-100 cm range. The colour film in use will also be a contributing factor, some being 'warmer' than others.

Undoubtedly, electronic flash is the more convenient form of lighting, and is cheaper in the long run. It does, however, require a pressure-proof housing of its own, and reliable waterproof connections from unit to camera. For close-up work, there is a bewildering choice of small electronic flash units which are relatively easy to house, and provide sufficient light output for successful photographs at distances of up to one metre.

If this brief introduction has given you the urge to try underwater photography, it will have accomplished its purpose. With increasing plundering and pollution of the world's oceans, you may one day find yourself with a photograph of a species that has gone the way of the dodo.

References

Fryer G. and Iles T.D. *The Cichlid Fishes of the Great Lakes of Africa* Oliver and Boyd, Edinburgh 1971

Halstead B.W. *Dangerous Marine Animals* Cornell Maritime Press, Cambridge, Maryland 1959

Lorenz K. *On Aggression* University Paperback Edition, 1972 Reprint

Marshall T. *Tropical Fishes of the Great Barrier Reef* Angus and Robertson, London 1966

Smith J.L.B. 'Coral fishes of the family Pomacentridae from the Western Indian Ocean and the Red Sea' *Ichthyological Bulletin No.* 19 Department of Ichthyology, Rhodes University, Grahamstown 1960

Smith J.L.B. 'The fishes of the family Gaterinidae in the Red Sea and the Indian Ocean, with a résumé of all Indo-Pacific species' *Ichthyological Bulletin No.* 25 Department of Ichthyology, Rhodes University, Grahamstown 1962

Smith J.L.B. *The Sea Fishes of Southern Africa* Central News Agency, South Africa. Fifth Edition 1965

Smith J.L.B. and Smith M.M. *The Fishes of Seychelles* The J.L.B. Smith Institute of Ichthyology, Rhodes University, Grahamstown. Second Edition 1969

Index